WELDING ALCOA ALUMINUM

Alcoa maintains complete facilities for research and development of new welding alloys and materials. Also, the Alcoa Process Development Laboratory in New Kensington, Pa. is staffed and equipped to assist customers on the engineering and production aspects of their welding problems. These pictures show some of the facilities used in this work.

WELDING
ALCOA ALUMINUM

Aluminum Company of America

Pittsburgh, Pennsylvania

Foreword

During a fairly short time, many changes in the technology of welding aluminum alloys have occurred. New methods and improved techniques have reached commercial importance. At the same time, some of the pioneering methods have been relegated to narrower fields of application.

This booklet reflects such changes. In addition to basic, practical data on the individual processes, it includes information on choice of method to assist welding engineers, shop men and designers at that important stage in the job when decisions are being formulated.

The predecessor to this booklet was titled *Welding and Brazing Alcoa Aluminum*. Now, brazing is to be treated separately in *Brazing Alcoa Aluminum*.

Some of the materials and methods discussed in this book are covered by patents or patent applications owned by Aluminum Company of America or by others, including welding equipment suppliers. Nothing herein should be construed as an invitation to use such methods or materials without proper arrangements.

Tabular data and descriptive text in this book should answer most routine questions about welding aluminum alloys. But we realize that many problems will still need individual attention.

We cordially invite you to get in touch with your local Alcoa sales office if you need further information or guidance. Our sales representatives will find a solution to your problem if they can. If not, they will call on Alcoa specialists and laboratory scientists to get the facts you need.

Table of Contents

Welding is one method used to join aluminum in today's aircraft.

Welding makes possible the development of graceful aluminum furniture.

Introduction to Welding Alcoa Aluminum Alloys

Sound, reliable welds have been made in aluminum alloys for many years. Welded joints are strong. Decades of service under widely different conditions can be cited to demonstrate their high quality.

Millions of beverage, food and chemical containers, cooking utensils, many kinds of pressure vessels, structural components, process equipment, tanks for railroad cars—examples of welded aluminum are almost everywhere. Resistance welding is a useful assembly method in aircraft manufacture—and in many other fields.

Improvements have widened the scope of welding. In the past, the nonheat-treatable alloys of aluminum were welded extensively. Now, the stronger alloys are welded too. Great strides have been made in overcoming difficulties with cracking, brittleness and loss of desirable mechanical properties.

Now, new equipment and better techniques are available to bring more of the Alcoa aluminum alloys into the "readily weldable" category. At the same time, progress is still being made to speed up the operation, to eliminate unnecessary procedures, and to develop mechanized equipment for high-speed repetitive production. Because of continual process development, aluminum is now as easy to weld and as generally weldable as steel.

A dump-truck body welded of aluminum stands up under abusive service conditions, and the weight it saves will make bigger loads possible every trip.

Some of the advances involve arc welding—without flux—in an envelope of inert gas. Either a tungsten electrode or a consumable, aluminum alloy electrode is used. Resistance welding, too, continues to grow in importance. As the process becomes better understood it is applied more widely and successfully.

Gas welding was the pioneer method of welding aluminum and is used extensively today. Atomic hydrogen welding is employed for important aluminum welding jobs. A new method that involves no molten metal—pressure welding—may hold important commercial possibilities.

Massive aluminum pieces, such as these pipe flanges, can be welded.

These aluminum utensils all have welded joints. Handles and bottom are welded on the tub, the handle on the milk can, leg brackets and handle sockets to the vegetable press, spouts on the coffee makers and coffee server, and the handle socket is welded to the frying pan.

This book describes the various types of aluminum welding and provides technical and practical data. We hope the combination will be most useful.

Brazing—the companion method to welding—is the topic of *Brazing Alcoa Aluminum,* another book in this series.

Where welding should be selected for making joints in aluminum

Before discussion of which welding method to choose, it may be helpful to outline briefly where welding itself offers greatest benefits. Here are some practical design considerations that may lead to the decision to weld a joint in aluminum instead of brazing, soldering, resin bonding, using rivets, bolts, special fasteners, or making other design provisions.

Welds prevent leaks. One of the easiest ways to make a permanent gas-tight or liquid-tight joint is by fusion welding or resistance seam welding. Hence, all kinds of aluminum tanks, pressure vessels, pipelines, containers, and the like are welded.

Welds can be made in thick or thin metal. Fusion welds can be made in material several inches thick without difficulty. Thin metal —less than ⅟₁₆ inch—is often fusion welded. Resistance welding is highly satisfactory down to foil gages. Bars, rods, wire and special extruded sections can be joined readily by fusion or flash welding.

The user has a wide choice of welding equipment and welding methods. He can set up to make one piece or tens of thousands. Simple, relatively inexpensive hand equipment will accommodate a wide variety of jobs—in the shop or field. On the other hand, modern aluminum welding methods lend themselves to complete automation. Jigs and assembly fixtures for simultaneous welding can turn out elaborate assemblies in mass production quantities.

Speed and cost compete with other joining methods when allround performance is the basis for comparison. In each case, the actual cost depends on the kind of job and quantities involved.

Welding is versatile. Repair work, and maintenance, of course, are common occasions for welding aluminum. Equipment can be brought to the job.

Castings can be welded as a production assembly method, as a foundry operation for minor modification and to correct defects, or as a repair procedure for restoring worn and broken parts to service.

Resistance to corrosion is good because both parent and weld metal are aluminum. Under severe conditions, special precautions can be taken to obtain satisfactory resistance to corrosion.

Finished welds can be smooth. Welding makes possible single-piece construction of complicated aluminum articles. A welded joint can be finished to match the parent metal. A ground and polished weld can be given an anodic finish along with other aluminum surfaces. Sometimes special procedures may be advisable to match colors.

Welding saves material and reduces the weight of many stressed assemblies. A butt weld is a symmetrical joint, and when finished smooth, it presents no stress-raising irregularities.

All-welded aluminum alloy tanks are made for oils, fatty acids and other process materials.

2

Factors to consider
when selecting
a welding method

Aluminum can be welded by a number of processes. Many of these processes are used commercially. Each one has certain advantages. Here is a summary of the methods that are most likely to be of interest.

Gas Welding employs an oxyacetylene, oxyhydrogen or other fuel gas flame to melt parent metal—and usually filler metal—to make a weld.

Metal arc welding is the common process wherein the arc between a flux-coated electrode and the work heats both the electrode and the work, and deposits electrode metal to form a weld bead.

Carbon arc welding utilizes an arc between a carbon electrode and the work for heat. Added filler metal is usually provided.

Atomic hydrogen welding is done with a special torch that maintains an arc independently of the work. Heat is conveyed to the weld by molecular breakdown and recombination of hydrogen that flows through the arc.

Inert gas tungsten arc welding uses heat from an arc between the work and a non-consumable tungsten electrode. The arc is enveloped by a stream of inert gas. No flux is needed.

Inert gas consumable electrode welding is metal arc welding that employs an automatically-fed, bare electrode. The arc is enveloped by a stream of inert gas. No flux is needed.

Spot welding is a resistance welding method that forms localized areas of cast metal between work pieces by combining the heat of resistance to electric current with the application of mechanical pressure.

Seam welding is a special form of spot welding in which a row of spots is made with precise control so that the welds can, if required, overlap to form a pressure-tight seam.

Flash welding applies heat by establishing an arc between the pieces to be joined. Then they are forced together at a predetermined rate to squeeze out the excess molten metal and to consolidate the joint.

Pressure welding is done by applying pressure to suitably prepared surfaces below the melting point of the parts.

Selection of method is based on many considerations

The conditions that influence a choice of method will be familiar to experienced welding engineers. Not necessarily in the order of importance they include:

> —thickness and size of parts
> —location and position of weld
> —number of similar welds
> —production rate required
> —investment in welding equipment
> —finish and appearance desired
> —type of aluminum alloy

Thick sections that require multiple passes to form a bead are best welded with an inert gas shielded arc using a consumable electrode. Sections of moderate thickness—for example, between $\frac{1}{16}$ and $\frac{3}{16}$ inch—can be welded by any of the commercial processes. Resistance spot or seam welding is used successfully with metal thicknesses from foil up to $\frac{3}{16}$ inch. Pieces up to $\frac{1}{2}$ inch thick are being spot welded experimentally. See Table 1.

Metal Thickness Ranges
for Commercial Welding Practice

Table 1

Welding Method	Minimum metal thickness, inch		Maximum metal thickness, inch
	Experimental	Ordinary practice	
Inert gas shielded consumable electrode .	.032	.093	①
Inert gas shielded tungsten electrode . .	.025	.051	1
Gas	.025	.051	1
Atomic hydrogen	.025	.051	1
Metal arc	.064	.125	①
Spot	—	foil	³⁄₁₆①
Seam	foil	.010	³⁄₁₆

①No limit imposed by the welding process. While any practical thickness can be welded, most experience so far has been on pieces up to 3 inches thick.
②Experimental procedures have been developed for metal up to ½-inch thickness.

Location of welds will affect the choice of welding method, depending on whether work is done in shop or field and on the welding position for individual joints.

Gas welding equipment is highly portable. Resistance welding equipment, on the other hand, is usually permanently installed. Metal arc welding requires only a standard motor-driven dc welding generator. Inert gas shielded methods require a gas supply plus more elaborate welding machines.

Inert gas shielded arc welding can be carried out in all positions, including overhead. Other fusion methods depend on floating oxides out of the weld as slag, and they are limited to the downhand, horizontal, and—sometimes—vertical positions.

The number of similar welds to be made or the number of similar pieces to be handled will influence tooling in general. Mass-production quantities justify making an investment in elaborate jigs and fixtures, mechanized equipment and automatic welding controls. So, also, do lesser quantities that fall considerably below what industry would term "mass" production. Welding methods that lend themselves to automation are the inert gas processes, atomic hydrogen and all the resistance welding methods.

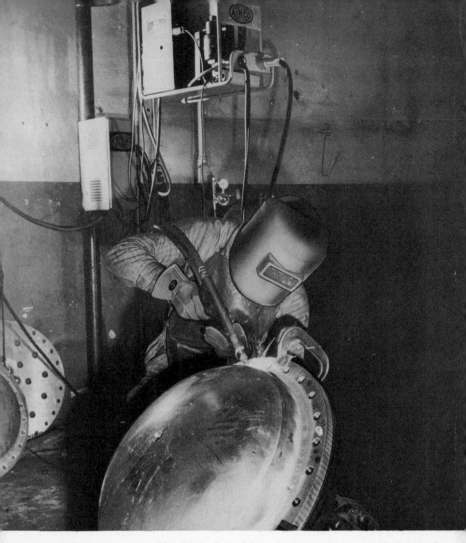

Inert gas, consumable electrode welding on the head for a fuel filter tank of 3S aluminum.

At the other extreme are welds for repair or for construction of individual units. Here, gas welding is often employed because of the simplicity of equipment involved. Inert gas shielded arc welding offers the distinct advantage of not contaminating a job with corrosive flux that has to be removed. Of course, shops that have other types of hand equipment available will use it instead of purchasing the ideal setup for each small job.

Production rates are usually linked with elaborateness of tooling, and this factor has its effect on choice of process. However, even with hand welding, there are marked variations in output. The amount of work done is sometimes influenced more by the skill and experience of the welding operator than by the choice of method. Inert gas metal arc welding, with its automatically fed consumable electrode, is interesting in this respect because it sets a pace for a welding operator.

Investment in welding equipment in a modest-sized shop may make the question of choosing methods a purely academic one. Many sorts of work can be done with the equipment available. All of the commercial methods for welding Alcoa Aluminum are versatile. Each can be adapted to handle a wide variety of work satisfactorily.

Finish and appearance of welds can be tailored to the needs of each situation. Gas welding usually produces a bead that can be finished smooth with a minimum number of flaws and rejects. Hence, this method finds wide application for welding products like aluminum cooking utensils and furniture, where smoothness and appearance must be excellent. Tungsten arc welding, though more costly than gas welding, may sometimes save in over-all cost where cleanliness and soundness of welds are of paramount importance.

Alloy selection depends on a number of factors besides welding

Usually, but not always, a particular aluminum alloy is chosen on the basis of its mechanical strength. Mechanical properties of all the commercially standard Alcoa aluminum alloys, both in wrought and cast forms, are shown in Tables 4 and 6. See pages 124-125, 128-129 and notes following each table. Other physical properties that are useful and important when considering the welding of these materials are also listed.

Alcoa produces these alloys in all of the common commercial forms—sheets, tubes, rolled and extruded shapes, castings, etc.—though not all the alloys and tempers are made in all the forms. Write or call your nearest Alcoa sales office to obtain information

19

on price and availability of a specific alloy and temper. See page 176 to find the location of the Alcoa sales office nearest you.

In many cases, factors other than strength are equally important in choosing an alloy for a specific application. Another major consideration is the resistance of joints to corrosion. Both strength and resistance of welds to corrosion are covered in detail in Chapter 11, page 95.

Forming operations used to make the part frequently dictate both the aluminum alloy and its temper. Material price may also be a factor. Availability of equipment in a fabricator's plant may have a bearing on the choice. When the material and the welding equipment are already chosen at the start of a job, as is frequently the case, the welding method and procedures are adapted to the specific conditions.

Selection of welding method and alloy when parts will be Alumilite finished

Another consideration—and one that may influence the choice of alloy—is the appearance of weld zones on parts that are to be Alumilite* finished. This finishing method produces apparent color changes in and near the weld zone. Occasionally such differences are objectionable.

Least contrast between the weld zone and parent metal after Alumilite finishing is obtained with the nonheat-treatable wrought alloys. Heat-treatable alloys 61S, 62S and 63S are frequently used in architectural work, and they are often Alumilite finished. The heat of welding causes precipitation of alloying constituents in these alloys. Thus, after Alumilite finishing, the heat-affected area may exhibit a different appearance near each welded joint. This color difference can be minimized by solution heat treatment of the parts to redissolve constituents after welding. This operation is costly and is frequently impractical.

---

* Alumilite is a trade name of Aluminum Company of America. It identifies processes for the anodic oxidation of aluminum. The resulting Alumilite finishes confer increased hardness and durability upon the metal. Further information can be obtained from the nearest Alcoa sales office.

One pass was made from each side of every butt joint with a consumable-electrode hand gun to assemble 2S plate into 20-foot diameter tanks.

In many instances, other means of controlling the extent and severity of the discoloration are employed.

The method of welding has some effect. Experience has shown that joints made by torch welding, metal arc welding or inert gas shielded arc welding appear about the same *in the weld metal* after Alumilite finishing.

Inert gas shielded arc welded joints generally minimize the "halo" or staining effect *near the weld zone*. Arc welding deposits metal rapidly with a narrow heat-affected area.

Torch brazing, incidentally, with its application of more moderate heat for extensive periods of time results in a very gradual temperature differential. Arc welding or torch brazing results in less discoloration than torch welding.

Flash butt welding makes the narrowest weld zone and results in the least discoloration caused by rise of metal temperature near the weld. Welds made by this method show a narrow line at the joint that nearly matches the parent metal. Equipment and machine setups for making flash welds are relatively expensive and use of the process is limited to production of large numbers of similar pieces.

The type of mechanical finish affects discoloration. Coarser mechanical finishes lessen color differences on Alumilite finished welded parts. A sand belt or steel wool finish is much better than buffed or polished finishes.

A thinner Alumilite coating has limitations when this expedient is attempted as a way to control discoloration. The thickness of anodic coating should always be specified with a view to service requirements of the part.

The composition of welding wire has a definite effect on the color matching between welds and parent metal. For instance, welds made with 2S or A54S filler wire are about the same color as 61S, 62S, or 63S. Some contrast between the weld and parent metal shows, however, because the cast metal in the weld has a different texture from the wrought parent metal. Similar results can be obtained by employing strips of parent metal as filler wire, but this may lead to difficulty from cracking. A preliminary trial is advisable to determine whether the parent composition will work out as a filler material in each case.

The color of Alumilite finish on a weld made with 43S wire is dark gray compared to the parent metal. Consequently, 43S filler shows a greater contrast in color than the alloys mentioned in the previous paragraph. Torch brazed joints are made with No. 718 Brazing Wire, which, like 43S, is a silicon alloy. This material also turns dark gray upon Alumilite finishing. In the case of brazing, however, as contrasted with welding, the parent metal is not melted when the joint is made. When the excess metal is removed, only a regular, narrow line of filler metal appears on the surface. The appearance of this line is frequently not objectionable.

Location of the weld bead can often be changed to afford both satisfactory joint strength and freedom from discoloration. The weld can be made from the back or under side of the assembly by the metal arc process, inert gas shielded arc process, or by torch brazing. If equipment for all three methods is available, the best recommendation would be inert gas shielded arc welding. Next best would be torch brazing, since this reduces the chance of melting the base metal or "burning through." Wide distribution of temperature usually eliminates the staining or "halo" effect. Torch welds, on the other hand, when made from the under side, result in discoloration of the top surface.

The thickness of the parts determines to a certain extent the speed of welding and, consequently, the distribution of heat during welding. Generally, thin parts can be welded more readily in shorter time periods and with less discoloration than heavy parts of similar alloy and temper.

Tungsten arc welding was used to assemble these Alclad 3S water pipes.

Vessels for low-temperature fractionation of air which were tungsten arc welded in a shielding atmosphere of argon gas.

3

Inert Gas Shielded
Metal Arc Welding
with Tungsten Electrode

One of the biggest advances in aluminum welding has been the development of metal arc methods that do not require flux. Using an inert gas to keep air away from the arc and away from the molten metal makes this possible. Even though inert gas shielded arc welding imposes a need for more complex equipment, as compared to some of the other methods, the advantages it affords have justified its widespread adoption and use.

The rather wordy nomenclature of the above chapter title is usually shortened in various ways to give this method a convenient name. Some of the common terms are proprietary trade names owned by welding equipment suppliers. In this booklet, we have named this method "tungsten arc" welding or "inert gas tungsten arc" welding for the sake of brevity.

Advantages of tungsten arc welding are based on freedom from the need for flux—either on the work or on filler metal when used.

With no flux present welds do not have to be cleaned. Difficult-to-reach places or completely inaccessible interiors of welded assemblies will not have any flux contamination to act as a potential source of corrosion.

High-pressure process equipment of aluminum built with tungsten arc welding.

Furthermore, tungsten arc welding can be done in all positions. There is no slag to be worked out of the weld by gravity or by puddling. Overhead welding is entirely feasible. This solves practical problems when it is difficult or impossible to position the work.

Visual control is good. The gas envelope around the arc is transparent, and the weld puddle is clean. A welder doing a hand welding job can make a neater, sounder weld because he does not have to contend with smoke and fumes and can see what he is doing.

Minimum distortion of the metal near the weld is a big advantage gained by concentrating the heat. Among all the precautions that can be taken to prevent weld cracking or locked-up stresses, concentrated heat ranks first. The intensity of the tungsten arc is in the order of 10,000 to 15,000 amperes per square inch of electrode.

Argon and helium are the inert gases used

There is little difference in soundness or strength of welds whether argon or helium is employed. With helium, penetration of the weld is deeper. Hence it is often employed for higher speeds and thicker sections. However, argon finds more general use than helium because it affords better control of the weld pool and of the arc. There is less clouding, and the metal stays brighter in an argon envelope—hence, the operator can see the weld pool more clearly.

The welding head, or gun, has a cup around the tungsten electrode. It is water cooled to keep the electrode from melting. Flow of inert gas out of the cup is maintained during welding, so that the arc and the weld pool are completely surrounded, and air is excluded.

Why the welder needs certain features

Even a high-temperature material like tungsten will be consumed in the arc if it gets hot enough. Hence, there are limits to the current-carrying capacity of the tungsten electrode. These limits,

Automatic equipment makes tungsten arc welding a high-production process.

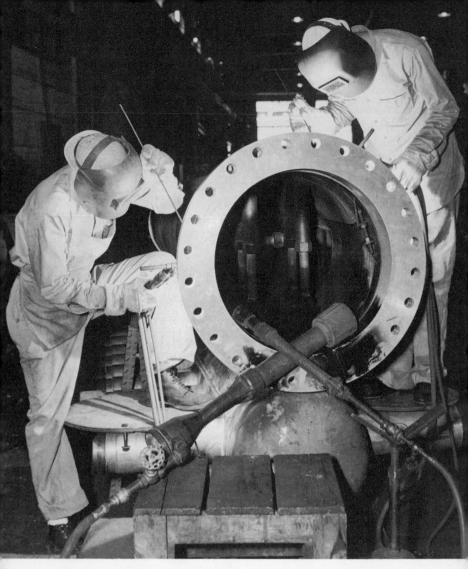

Two gas torches are employed here to preheat the work while the flange is being welded.

coupled with heating characteristics of the work in terms of polarity, have led to the use of alternating current for almost all tungsten arc welding. The size of the electrode is determined by the current which, in turn, is a function of the material thickness. Recommended sizes for many welding combinations are shown in Tables 8 to 12.

As alternating current reverses direction, it goes through zero twice each cycle. The ac arc would not normally persist through the zero points of current reversal. The arc would simply go out. Also, it would be virtually impossible to establish an arc on a cold electrode unless assisted in some way. This assistance is provided in the form of an auxiliary "sparking" voltage. A high-frequency oscillator in the welding equipment superimposes a low-current stabilizing voltage on the welding circuit. This high-frequency energy may be applied all the time during welding if the welder has low open-circuit voltage characteristics. Machines with higher open-circuit voltage and specially designed stabilizing circuits may use a short burst of high-frequency energy to start the arc.

Radio interference is a possible by-product of the sparking voltage. Unless properly shielded and grounded, the high-frequency circuit can generate interference that may affect radio and television reception. Installation and grounding instructions for the specific machine should be followed in detail.

Because tungsten arc welding demands special features in equipment, it is recommended that a welding machine designed for the purpose by its manufacturer be employed. Modifying a general-purpose welder is not usually economical.

Filler rods and joint preparation

Sometimes enough parent metal is provided by the design of the joint to form the weld bead. The extra metal may be on a corner or flange that is melted to form the weld.

Usually, filler metal is added—in bare rod form for hand welding or as a coil of wire for automatic feeding. This added metal is fed into the molten pool where the arc supplies heat to melt it. Recommended size of filler rod and consumption data are shown in Tables 8 to 12, pages 132 to 139.

A choice of alloy for filler rod depends on the aluminum alloy to be welded. For welding 2S or 3S parts, 2S filler rod is usually used. Alcoa 43S filler rod is a widely used filler material for welding alloys like 4S, 52S, 53S, 61S, 62S or 63S, for combinations of these alloys, or for welding these alloys to 2S or 3S. The wide variety of joints required in building construction and other architectural applications usually indicates the use of Alcoa 43S filler rod. Special-purpose welding, such as work that must be Alumilite finished, requires certain precautions as described in Chapter 2, page 20.

Welding of 4S, 52S and A54S alloys is frequently done with Alcoa A54S filler rod.

Joints made with this filler rod have excellent strength and the highest ductility that it is possible to achieve on welded joints in these alloys. Welds made in highly restricted locations, however, may show cracking when A54S rod is used. If this condition cannot be eliminated by adjustments of procedure or fixtures, then the cracking tendency can be reduced by using Alcoa 43S rod at some sacrifice in the ductility of the joint.

Assembly of vessels and drums to handle specific chemicals may require special welding rod. These applications frequently require the use of materials of higher purity than Alcoa 2S. Where this is the case, filler rod of equivalent purity should be used. Thus, where exposure tests have established the need for special composition control of the parent material to resist specific chemicals, the weld-

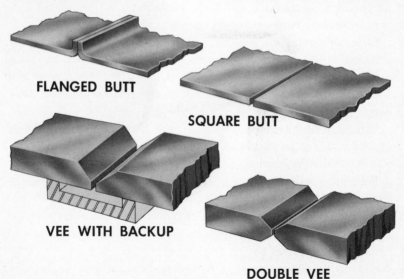

FLANGED BUTT

SQUARE BUTT

VEE WITH BACKUP

DOUBLE VEE

Fig. 1—Different edge preparations for tungsten arc welding. See Tables 8 to 12, pages 132 to 139, for specific dimensions and other data.

ing rod should be made to the same special composition limits. We invite inquiry to Aluminum Company of America for information on specific applications. Our wide experience in this field may provide a ready answer to your problems.

Joint preparation includes trimming, forming and clamping to insure good fit-up of parts. If jigs are not used to hold parts in correct relationships, use tack welds.

See Fig. 1 and the sketches with Tables 8 to 12 for specific recommendations. Material more than ⅛ inch thick is grooved to assure complete weld penetration.

Back-up bars of steel or stainless steel are recommended where welding will be done from one side only.

Cleanliness is important

In tungsten arc welding, there is no flux to absorb impurities. Combustible materials in the path of the arc will burn and generate gas that contaminates the inert envelope. This contamination causes scum to form over the molten metal and makes it difficult for the welding operator to obtain smooth flow of weld metal. It is also a potential cause of unsound welds.

Clean all parts of oil, grease and dirt. Vapor or solvent degreasing will usually be satisfactory. Parts can be cleaned by swabbing with a solvent-soaked rag. Take care not to use this method with solvents that involve a health hazard. If heavy oxide is present on the metal surface, it may be necessary to use mechanical means—such as wire brushing—to achieve cleanliness. Chemical cleaning will also take care of severe conditions. The etchants described on page 49 are suitable for chemical cleaning.

Preheating parts to be welded may be advantageous. It can reduce over-all costs. First, the reduced temperature difference between weld and surrounding metal makes it possible for the operator to do the work more easily. Second, he can work faster because parts come up to welding temperatures more rapidly. Preheat temperatures range between 400° and 800°F. For vertical and overhead welding, the higher preheat temperatures afford better control of the arc and of the weld pool.

Automatic operation of tungsten arc welding is highly successful. A number of arrangements are possible. Most of them include power-driven traversing mechanisms for the jigged parts or the welding head, and interlocked controls for the high-frequency starting circuit, welding current, and flow of shielding gas.

The cost of automatic equipment is not hard to justify if the amount of welding to be done is large and if the work is suitable. Barrels have been produced in great quantities by tungsten arc welding aluminum in automatic machines. Tanks of many sizes are welded in machines that can accommodate size differences along with some variation in locations of welds.

In hand welding, one precaution should be emphasized more than any other. Keep the arc short—about the same length as the tungsten electrode diameter. An important reason for a short arc is to make sure that inert gas completely surrounds the weld as it forms.

Strike the arc by swinging the gun in a pendulum-like motion toward the starting place. Strike it like a match. After a molten

Application of the inert gas shielded tungsten arc for welding fittings to an aircraft gasoline tank.

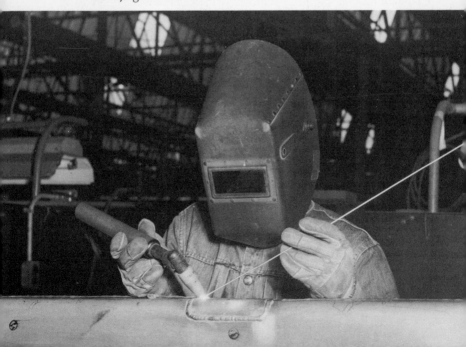

pool forms, move steadily along the seam with the gun positioned as shown in the picture on page 32.

Finishing the weld bead improves appearance and sanitation. In food handling and chemical equipment, a smooth weld is desired because it can be easily cleaned. Butt welds may be dressed by using a pneumatic chisel to chip the edge of the weld bead almost flush with the surface of the parent metal, then finished with a hammer to provide a smooth flush surface. This differs from the conventional peening process in that the weld is worked with heavy blows to cold work the complete cross section rather than the surface layer only.

Fillet and corner welds are finished by grinding or filing. Conventional grinding wheels can be kept from loading up by employing a heavy grease lubricant. Felt wheels may also be used. Grinding compound is applied to felt wheels by rolling the edge of the wheel in glue, then rolling in abrasive compound graded in fineness from 60 to 200, depending on the surface required on the finished part. Buffing and color operations are performed on welds in the same manner as on the parent metal.

Tungsten arc welding can be performed in any position and there is no flux to be removed. Both features are valuable when making pipe joints.

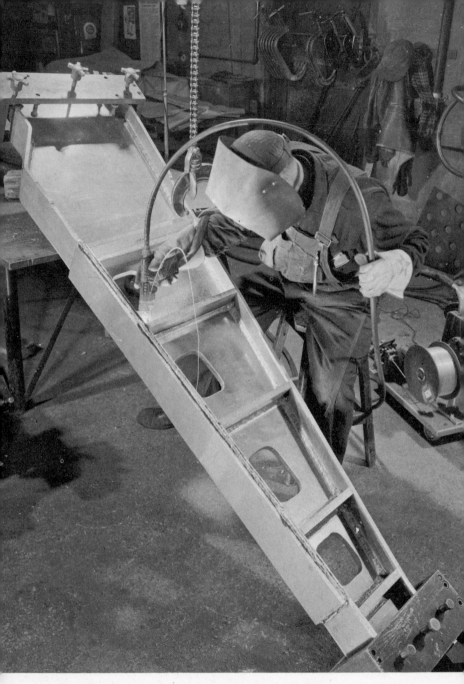

*Sound welds can be made with speed and cleanliness using standard con-
sumable electrode equipment.*

4

Inert Gas Shielded
Metal Arc Welding
with Consumable Electrode

Development of metal arc welding with a consumable, uncoated aluminum electrode in an inert gas atmosphere has significantly widened the application of welding aluminum alloys.

Consumable electrode welding, as we shall term this method for the sake of brevity, offers the same advantages as tungsten arc welding. And, it has some unique virtues of its own.

The method is fast. Not only is a great amount of heat concentrated in a small area, but the consumable electrode is fed at a pre-set speed.

Sound welds with good surface appearance and shape are easy to make. There is almost no spatter. Subsequent finishing is made cheaper and easier.

Any welding position is practical for consumable electrode welding. Vertical and overhead welding are completely feasible.

No flux is required, thus, post-cleaning cost and difficulties are avoided.

Arc energy is high. Consumable electrode welding concentrates more heat than any of the other fusion welding methods. Current densities in the electrode are in the order of 50,000 to 100,000 am-

Inert gas, consumable electrode welding thick plate sections for a diesel engine bed.

peres per square inch. Problems of distortion, cracking and metallurgical change are reduced to a minimum.

Dc welding machines are employed

Good results can be achieved either with rotating machines or with rectifier equipment. Standard motor-generator sets used for welding other metals are suitable for consumable electrode welding. Extensive use of dry-disk rectifier equipment, also usable for other metals, has proved successful.

Electrically, the welding machine should be capable of maintaining a stable arc down to 50 volts. A capacity of 400 to 500 amperes will be adequate for almost all jobs.

A high-speed welding contactor for a rotary generator or a switch on the primary of a dry-disk rectifier-type machine is provided. Thus, the welding circuit is de-energized while the welding operation is not actually going on.

Reverse polarity—electrode positive—is almost always used.

A source of 115-volt, 60-cycle power is needed to drive the electrode feed mechanism. When this requirement is met, an engine-driven dc welder is thoroughly suitable for consumable electrode welding of aluminum.

Self contained consumable electrode welding equipment that will operate independently of power or water source. It is used for field welding work.

The **shielding gas** can be either helium, argon, or a mixture of the two. No clear-cut advantage in gas cost under commercial welding conditions has been established for either gas. The essential difference is that welds shielded with helium penetrate 10 to 20 per cent deeper than is the case with argon. This can be used to advantage only on high speed automatic welding. In most work, the performance of either gas will be about the same.

Joint preparation includes strict cleanliness—as it does for tungsten arc welding. Any gas or other by-product of combustion formed by foreign matter in the arc will be a potential contaminant of the weld.

Clean all surfaces with vapor or solvent degreasing equipment, by swabbing with solvent, by wire brushing, or by chemical means, if necessary. Thin pieces can merely be butted together with a good fit. If they are to be welded from one side only in flat position, a backup piece of steel or stainless steel will allow full and controlled weld penetration. Copper is not suitable because it can contaminate the weld if the arc goes through to the backup bar. The resulting bad spots of aluminum-copper alloy are brittle and sensitive to corrosion.

If welding can be done from both sides, the conventional back-chipping technique is used. A groove is chipped out along the back side of the bead before welding this side. For specific information and recommendations refer to Tables 13 to 16.

The electrode wire is specially prepared

Electrode wire used in this process is relatively small—.030 to .093 inch in diameter for semi-automatic guns, depending on work thickness. Its special preparation usually involves cold drawing and level winding. A feed mechanism takes this bare aluminum wire off a reel at a constant rate. It pushes the wire through a guide passage in the flexible conduit, which also contains an electrical conductor, cooling water passages, and a passage for flow of the inert gas. Some types of equipment pull the wire through the guide passage, using a feed mechanism at the gun, which is driven by a flexible shaft.

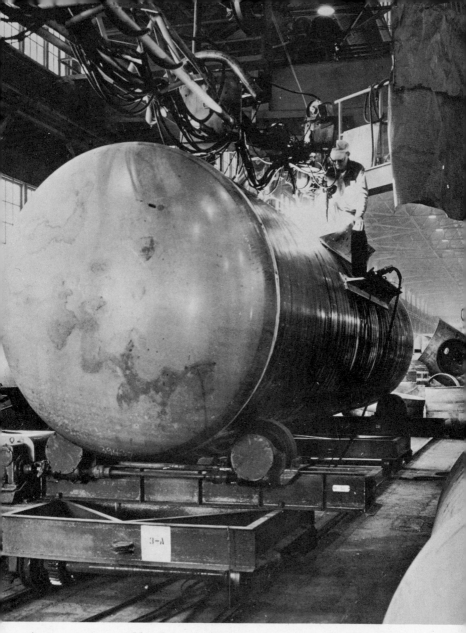

Automatic consumable electrode welding of the tank anchorage for a railroad tank car. Here, the welding head remains stationary while the tank moves longitudinally.

*Overhead welding—a necessity where piping is joined in its final position
—presents no problem for consumable electrode welding.*

The electrode emerges from its holder and is consumed as fast as it comes out. The fact that a relatively long wire must pass through a flexible guide and out of the gun raises a possibility of trouble from buckling or jamming. With semi-automatic welding, small wire and continual movement increase the chance of jamming the wire—especially with the types of equipment that push it instead of pulling. To prevent this difficulty, it is good practice to position the work to provide as straight-line feeding of the electrode as possible. Furthermore, for the smaller wire sizes, drawn and level-wound electrode wire should be used.

Larger wire—up to ⅛-inch diameter—is used in automatic welding. It can usually be in the soft temper. For automatic welding, level winding on the reel is not of as much importance as it is in hand welding.

The aluminum alloy most used for electrode wire is Alcoa 43S. Practically all stock filler metal handled by distributors and supply houses is made from this alloy. Properly cleaned and reeled electrode wire can be obtained at most welding supply houses or by contacting your nearby Alcoa sales office.

Alcoa 2S electrode is used for welding 2S and 3S because it affords best ductility and strength. Similarly, 4S and 52S are often welded with A54S wire. Special-purpose applications may require consideration of other electrode alloys. Proper choice is made on the same basis as described for filler rod for tungsten arc welding on page 29.

Welding technique is somewhat different from those of other methods, but is not difficult to master. It does, however, require training. A new operator has to learn how to adjust the gun and how to use it for best and consistent results. If an operator is experienced at welding steel, he may need 20 to 40 hours' training before achieving a reliable competence at consumable electrode welding of aluminum.

The flow of gas, flow of cooling water, energizing of the welding circuit and feeding of the electrode wire are all started when the operator actuates his foot switch or trigger switch on the gun. He strikes the arc with a brushing motion—as one would strike a match.

Feed roll speeds should be set so that the electrode wire is con-

The use of consumable electrode arc welding with inert gas shielding in the fabrication of an aluminum tank for a trailer truck.

sumed as fast as it emerges from the gun without extending more than ⅜ inch beyond the edge of the gas nozzle.

Tilt the gun about 10 degrees forehand—pointed in the direction of progress along the bead. Straight passes give better results than the weaving motions used when welding steel.

5

Spot and Seam Welding

Resistance welding is today one of the most useful and practical methods of welding aluminum. Work pieces are pressed together between electrodes, and electrical resistance at the interface produces the welding heat when current is applied.

The economy of resistance welding arises from several factors. First, nothing is consumed except electric power. Second, the process is fast. Production has been quadrupled in some cases by redesigning parts for resistance welding. Third, less skilled personnel can perform the operation. The welding process is almost entirely automatic. In addition to these areas of economy, further savings are afforded by the fact that standard machines handle a wide variety of work—weld a wide range of thicknesses.

Because resistance welding heats only a small area of metal—and that for the minimum length of time—there is a minimum of metallurgical disturbance. Uniformly sound, dependable welds can be made. Spot and seam welding have gained importance in the manufacture of cooking utensils, of tanks—both for seams and for securing baffles of bridge flooring, and of many aircraft components. Such tasks as tacking wing skin sections, securing brackets, assembling cowling, making deck sections and the like are performed by spot welding.

Spot welding of handle brackets to aluminum cooking utensils is a high-production operation.

Many resistance welding applications are in aircraft work that is under government control. Here, equipment and welding procedures have to meet Military Specification MIL-W-6860. Anyone contemplating government work should obtain a copy of this specification.

Types of equipment
that are used for spot welding aluminum

Aluminum has specific properties, differing from those of other metals, that require different treatment in welding. For example, its high electrical and thermal conductivities mean that welding machines of high current capacity must be used to generate enough heat to melt the metal.

Aluminum welds have to be made fast to avoid dissipating heat into the work. Another specific difference—aluminum softens more than steel and some other metals during welding. Consequently, rapid set down of the metal tends to break off contact with the electrode. It is, of course, necessary to keep the tips in good contact. Massive parts cannot be made to follow sudden movements as easily as lighter ones can. Hence, low inertia in the electrode holder and a movable head has been found a desirable machine characteristic.

Except for these factors, resistance welding aluminum closely resembles the resistance welding of other metals.

Power supply is important. An ac spot welder imposes large momentary loads on the supply. These large, short-duration loads are single-phase, and because of the reactive character of the transformer circuit, the power factor is low.

Where power supply facilities are adequate, straight single-phase ac welders are used with timing controls on the transformer primary circuit. At the moment the weld is made, the demand of this type of machine may cause lights supplied by the same circuit to blink. The momentary voltage drop may interfere with operation of other machines on the same power line.

Such welder loads can create serious voltage disturbances where the plant power supply is not designed to handle them.* Welding machine manufacturers have faced this problem and have produced several kinds of equipment for utilizing three-phase power.

Electronic converters are used to supply low-frequency, single-phase power to the welder transformer. They utilize current from all three phases of the supply. Although the low-frequency current may be so short in duration as to constitute a single pulse, the current is reversed with each weld. This cancels out any residual flux in the transformer—an important precaution contributing toward consistency of the welds.

Dry-disk rectifiers are also used to convert three-phase power to single-phase dc. However, in this case, current flow at the tips is undirectional. The equipment is designed to prevent trouble from residual flux.

* Refer to: *Power Supply for Resistance Welding Machines*
        American Institute of Electrical Engineers
        33 W. 39th Street, New York 18, N.Y.

Three-phase welders offer advantages in that the over-all load is less, and the load per phase is considerably less. Compared to the demand of an ac welder, a three-phase welding machine draws only half as much current at a throat depth of 12 inches. At greater throat depths, it draws even less by comparison.

Electrostatic stored-energy welders have been built for welding aluminum, and many such machines are in use. These machines rectify three-phase power and store the energy in banks of capacitors. By taking a longer interval to accumulate the short-time energy of welding, such machines reduce peak demand.

A choice of resistance welder type, as a review of these welder characteristics shows, depends partly on the power supply—its voltage drop characteristics, demand limitations, whether or not lighting circuits are connected to the same feeder, and other considerations of this nature.

Clean surfaces are essential to good spot welding

Welds of uniformly high strength and good appearance depend on a low and consistent surface resistance between the work pieces. This means that surface oxides must not be heavy or non-uniform.

No fluxes are used during spot welding. Mechanical or chemical means are employed to prepare the surfaces when necessary. Whether cleaning has to be done depends on the grade of work and the nature of the metal.

For many products—like cooking utensils—the stock as received for welding is clean enough to afford adequate welds. Aircraft construction, by contrast, demands careful cleaning and continual checking of surface contact resistance.

Materials like 2S or 3S aluminum sheet seldom require cleaning. On the other hand, the more highly alloyed compositions and products like castings, extruded shapes, tubes, rolled structural shapes and forgings may need surface preparation.

Surface Resistance Measurements

The efficiency of the cleaning operations is determined by measuring the surface contact resistance. This measurement is used to

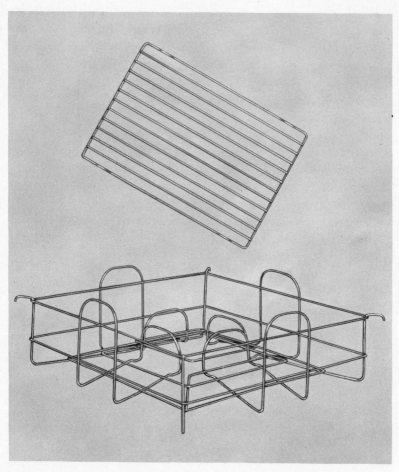

Practices for spot welding aluminum alloy wires have been developed.

determine the need for changes in the cleaning practices in order to insure consistent surface conditions on various lots of material as well as changes that are necessary with the different alloys. Best results are obtained when cleaning practices are established to obtain surface contact resistances below 50 microhms.

Surface contact resistance is measured by placing the material between two spot welding electrodes with 3-inch spherical radius dome shape. See Fig. 2. A standardized current and tip force are applied; 50 amperes direct current from storage batteries and a pressure of 600 pounds are frequently used. The resistance is established by measuring the potential drop with milli-voltmeters or using a Kelvin bridge. Commercial equipment for making the measurements under standardized test conditions is available.

The test is sensitive to small changes in procedure and values are usually obtained by averaging at least ten readings on an individual specimen. Movement of the specimen after the electrode pressure is applied will break the oxide coatings and will cause false readings. The presence of burrs on the specimens will also affect the accuracy of the test.

Cleaning and oxide removal begin with the removal of the stencil identification marks: This is best accomplished with alcohol or paint

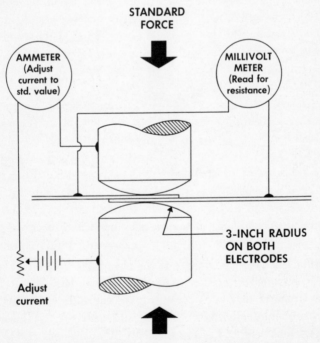

Fig. 2—Surface contact resistance between two pieces of aluminum is measured with standardized procedure and test equipment.

thinner. Then, degrease the piece with trichloroethylene or a benzene wash. Follow this by immersion in an etching solution of the following composition, used at 70° to 80°F:

Nitric acid (technical grade) (58–62% 39.5 Be)—110 to 120 grams per liter (1¾ oz per gal)

Hydrofluoric acid (technical grade, 48%)—3.5 to 4 grams per liter (6 oz per 100 gal)

Wetting agent, Nacconal NR or equivalent—2 grams per liter (3 oz per 100 gal)

Immerse the parts for 2 to 6 minutes in this solution at room temperature. Then rinse in clear, running cold water for 30 seconds. After that, a 10-second rinse in 140° to 160°F water can be used to speed drying. Dry in a warm air blast.

Parts like castings, forgings, extrusions and similar products that have heavy oxide films may need more severe cleaning, such as a caustic treatment. Immerse in 5 per cent sodium hydroxide at 150°F for 30 seconds and follow with a cold water rinse. Then, immerse in concentrated commercial nitric acid for not more than 30 seconds and rinse again in cold water. Rinse in hot water momentarily, and dry in hot air.

Proprietary materials and methods for removing aluminum oxides are available. Many of these are just as efficient as the cleaning methods described above.

When welding is confined to a small area, and the oxide film is not too thick, mechanical cleaning is often used successfully. It also lends itself for parts that are too large to be dipped and rinsed easily. Grease and dirt are first removed with solvent swabbing or by vapor degreasing. Then steel wool, abrasive cloth, or a power-driven wire brush may be employed. The wire brush should have stainless steel bristles .002 to .005 inch in diameter. A six-inch brush should rotate at 1800 to 3600 rpm.

It is not usually necessary to weld immediately after removing the oxide film. Parts may be held 48 hours or more, depending on the type of material, quality requirements of the work, and—especially—storage conditions. These factors vary, and the acceptable storage interval cannot be predicted.

Surface contact resistance is the guide. Testing of parts before welding will show whether they are clean enough. If resistance readings are high or inconsistent, surface preparation should be repeated.

Electrode contours must be carefully maintained for good results

Three functions are performed by the electrodes. First, they act as the conductors through which current is brought to the work pieces. Second, they exert sufficient force to hold the pieces in position to be welded. And, third, they serve to conduct heat away from the pieces being welded so that the heated zone does not extend to the outside surfaces of the material.

The principal consideration in maintaining tips is proper contour. In order to deliver a high current concentration at the weld, at least

Spot welding makes it practical to join formed pieces at a great many points to build strong, rigid, lightweight aluminum structures.

one of the tips must be rounded. Most resistance welding of aluminum is done with dome-shaped tips machined to a spherical contour. However, one of the tips may be flat if necessary to prevent indentation on one side. Only machining or dressing with a contoured dressing tool is sufficiently accurate for tip maintenance. Don't attempt to use a file.

Table 18 shows the tip dome radius for a variety of stock thicknesses and tempers. When pieces of different thickness are being welded, the tip radius tabulated for the thinner member is placed against that member. Poor welds will be obtained if a flat tip is used against the thinner piece.

For tip forces up to 3,000 pounds, it has been found satisfactory to use electrodes ⅝ inch in diameter seated with a No. 2 Morse taper. Over 3,000 pounds, electrodes ⅝ and ⅞ inch in diameter with an 8-degree taper should be used. Electrode materials for aluminum should be those listed in RWMA Group A, copper-base alloys, Classes 1 and 2. Hard-drawn copper electrodes make good welds, but they are prone to mushroom and prove difficult to maintain at the proper contour shape. Tungsten carbide or other special tip facings do not work well on the aluminum alloys.

To obtain the best duplication and maintenance of tips, dress them while they are on the machines. Wrap No. 180 or 240 abrasive cloth over a contoured steel dressing tool. Bring the tips together with a force of 100 to 200 pounds and rotate the tool. Then, clean the tips to remove any emery dust that may cling to them.

Electrode cooling controls pick-up and tip softening. Tap water circulated to within ⅜ inch of the tip face at a rate of at least 1 gallon per minute will be sufficient for most operations. When the tap water temperature goes above 60°F, refrigeration will be helpful in improving tip life. As a test, the electrodes should not feel warm after making five welds in rapid succession.

Design of joints for spot and seam welding

A comparison of the resistance welding characteristics of various alloys and tempers is shown in Table 17, page 148.

When designing joints, it is essential to provide work faces that can be placed in the machine normal to the axis of the electrodes, without touching any uninsulated part of the machine. Thus, parts must be so designed that the distance from the edge of the assembly to the weld does not exceed the throat depth of the available machine.

If the weld is too close to an edge, molten metal may squirt out from the joint. This occurrence, called "edge expulsion," will result in an unsound, weak weld. Edge-expulsion of the material welded can generally be avoided by providing sufficient overlap or flange width. Minimum recommended values are shown in Table 25. Welds with less than a 6t edge distance have low and inconsistent strength where "t" is the metal thickness.

The dimensions of the electrodes and electrode holders also influence the design of parts. For welding aluminum most work can be done with electrodes ⅝ inch in diameter and electrode holders 1¼ to 1½ inch in diameter. With these, the distance from the center of the weld to upstanding flanges should be as follows: ⁵⁄₁₆ inch where the flange height is 1 inch or less, and ⅝ to ¾ inch where the flange height is more than 1 inch.

Offset electrode holders are used to weld parts with overhanging flanges. The amount of offset that will be practical is limited by the force required and the strength and rigidity of the holders. Force is determined by the thickness of the material to be welded. Any appreciable deflection of the electrodes during welding results in slipping of the parts with consequent distortion of the welded assembly and poor quality welds.

When spot welds are closely spaced, a portion of the welding current will be shunted through previously-made welds. If the spacing is less than 8 times the thickness of the material, the current loss is sufficient to result in lowered weld strength. Two solutions are possible where it is necessary to space welds at less than 8t. One way is to increase the current after the first weld so as to offset the loss. Another, and more satisfactory way, is to use two or more rows of welds with the spaces in each limited to 8t. These result in welds of 85 to 90 per cent of the strength of an individual weld. The optimum number of spots per inch of joint may be determined by

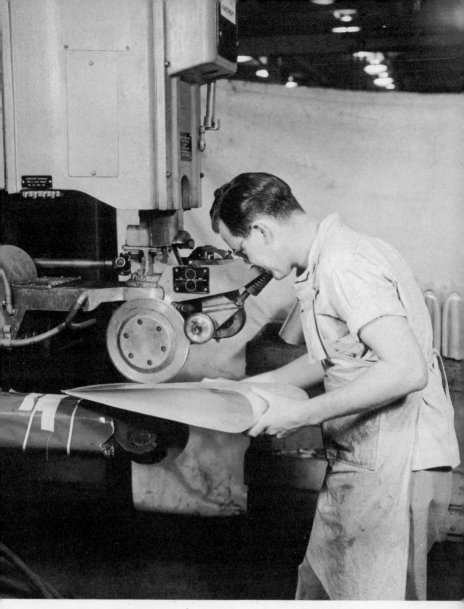

A seam welder can be set to make a row of spot welds for a strength joint, or a row of overlapping welds for a gas and liquid-tight seam.

dividing the strength of the material per linear inch by the average strength of the individual spot welds as obtained from Table 19. Joints so designed usually fail by tearing along the edge of the spots at joint efficiencies of 75 to 80 per cent.

The strength of spot welds will vary with the alloy and its thickness. Minimum shear strengths are given in Table 19, since spot welds are usually designed to carry shear loads.

Spot welds should be located so that the weld itself is under shear loading. However, in cases where tension or combined loadings are

Seam welding a large aircraft fuel tank tail section.

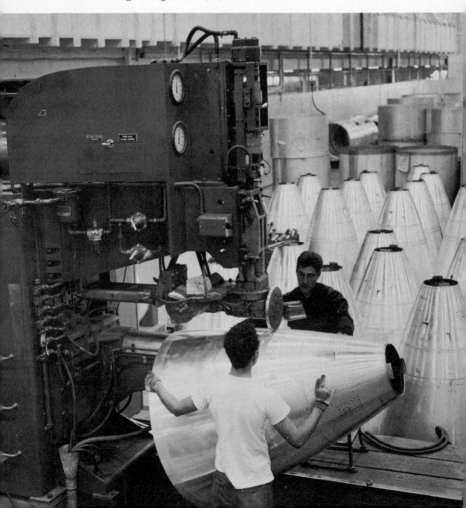

anticipated, don't count on a tensile strength greater than 25 per cent of the shear strength. Test an actual joint if heavy tension loads will be applied.

Using the settings shown in Tables 20, 21, 22 or 23, and producing a weld with a diameter equal to twice the thickness of the sheet plus ⅟₁₆ inch, the weld shear strength should exceed values in Table 19. Welds made on any of the kinds of equipment discussed earlier will have the same shear strengths provided the welds are of equal size. It is sometimes possible to obtain larger welds with energy storage equipment; the shear strength will then be proportionately larger. Welds of small size with strengths lower than those shown in the table should be avoided. Settings that give small diameter welds in aluminum are likely to result in a substantial number of "duds" under production conditions.

Know the defects and how to avoid them

Inspection and quality control procedures for aluminum spot welding are outlined briefly, and references are cited on pages 114 to 116 of Chapter 12.

Tip pick-up can occur with all types of welding equipment but may occur after making fewer spots with ac welding equipment than with other types of equipment. Pick-up may be caused by any of the following:

1. Surface contamination.
2. High surface resistance.
3. Incorrect tip contour.
4. Low tip force.
5. Excessively high energy level.
6. Poor fit.
7. Electrode deflection—skidding at tip.
8. Improper machine operation.

Cracks and porosity may be closely allied with pick-up. External cracks indicate a poor weld and can usually be eliminated by improved surface cleaning techniques. Internal cracks and porosity, detected by X-ray or sectioning methods are likewise associated with poor cleaning. These defects are also caused by the same

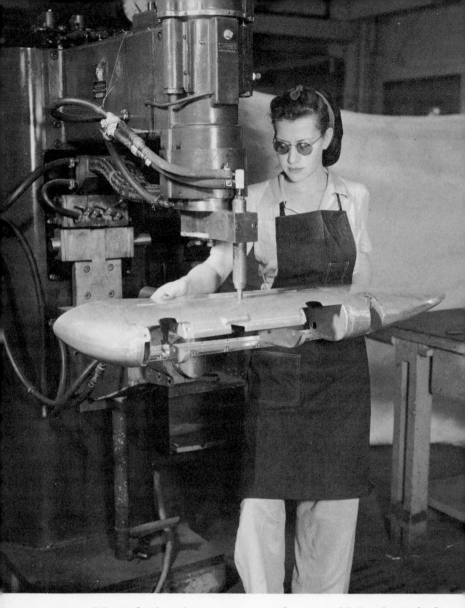

Many different kinds and sizes of parts can be spot welded with standard equipment like this.

faulty conditions listed above. Low tip force or the absence of forge force is a frequent cause of lack of weld soundness.

Incorrect weld penetration—either excessive or insufficient—is undesirable. It can be determined by sawing through the weld, smoothing with a file and a fine abrasive cloth, then etching with sodium hydroxide. Penetration between 20 and 80 per cent of the thickness is satisfactory, with 50 per cent the practical ideal. Tip radius is the determining factor. A smaller spherical radius increases penetration.

Sheet separation can be reduced by increasing the radius of the tip. When welding two equal gages, the sheet separation should not exceed 10 per cent of the sheet thickness. This condition is more difficult to control on the softer tempers of metal.

Expulsion of molten metal from the weld nugget can usually be eliminated by better cleaning methods. Another cause of expulsion is too low initial force followed by excessive forging pressure.

Excessive surface indentation arises from several causes. When it is caused by too soft a temper, there is little to do but change the material specification. Reducing the welding time, tip force and current, increasing the tip radius will also reduce the indentation.

Seam welding

Seam welding, or roller spot welding, is essentially the same as spot welding except that the machine makes spot welds at predetermined intervals. This interval may be adjusted so that the spots overlap, producing a pressure-tight seam.

In seam welding, electrodes are wheels with a diameter varying from 6 to 12 inches or larger. The electrode material should have a conductivity of no less than 75 per cent of copper and a hardness greater than Rockwell B-65. Wheel electrodes have two curvatures. One, determined by wheel radius, changes only slightly when the wheel is dressed. Transversely, the wheel is crowned with a radius according to Table 18.

Seam welding machines may use single-phase alternating current, condenser energy or three-phase alternating current. Current may be applied either when the wheels are moving or while they stop momentarily. The latter method results in a superior finish on the parts. As in other resistance welding methods, the electrodes are cooled. This may be accomplished either by cooling internally or by running water over the electrode, parts, or both.

Since some aluminum adheres to the electrodes, they must be cleaned by removing the accumulations of aluminum with a fairly coarse abrasive. A good general rule: on continuous seam welding, clean the wheels every three to five revolutions—on intermittent welding, every ten to twenty revolutions. Stored energy type equipment reduces the electrode pickup substantially; it is often possible to weld longer joints without cleaning than when using other types of equipment.

Adjust the welding pressure, current and timing to produce the desired spacing and a weld size twice the thickness of the material plus $\frac{1}{16}$ inch. Table 24 gives recommended welding schedules for aluminum alloys. It may be noted that the maximum "On" time is never greater than $\frac{1}{3}$ the total time. Less "On" time per weld helps reduce tip pickup, but it will also reduce nugget size.

In seam welding, the same defects occur for the same reasons as in spot welding. See page 55.

6

Flash Welding Butt and Miter Joints

All wrought aluminum alloys can be flash welded. Shapes of all kinds made from sheets, tubes, extrusions, wires, rods and bars may be joined. Usually the joint is a butt, but miter joints are flash welded, too. There are no inherent limitations on size or thickness of metal that can be flash welded, although equipment has not been developed so far to weld areas larger than about 3.5 square inches.

The parts to be flash welded are clamped in suitable dies on the welding machine, and an electric arc is established between the ends of the parts to be welded. The parts are moved together automatically to maintain the arc as metal is consumed. When the ends are hot enough, the weld is made by driving the ends together with enough speed and pressure to expel the molten material containing impurities. The parts are held in intimate contact until the joint has cooled.

High-quality joints by a mass-production process

The weld consists of a narrow cast zone of weld metal on either side of which is a very narrow zone of heat-affected and partially annealed metal. (See Fig. 3, page 60.) During the upsetting motion

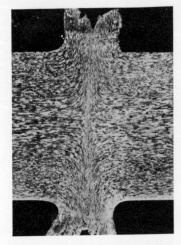

Fig. 3—Grain structure at the weld and shape of the flash of excess metal are shown on this etched specimen of welded ⅝-inch aluminum rod.

which occurs in making the weld, some hot working and some cold working occurs in the weld material and the heat-affected zone.

The mechanical properties of joints are good both in the nonheat-treatable and heat-treatable alloys. Joint efficiencies of at least 80 per cent on material in any temper are expected, and efficiencies of 100 per cent on the annealed alloys are obtained. Elongations measured across the weld on the nonheat-treatable alloys are about 50 per cent of the elongation of the parent material. In the heat-treated tempers of alloys such as 24S, 61S and 75S, expected weld strength is at least 80 per cent of the strength of the parent material, as noted above. The elongation at the weld is reduced to about 20 per cent of that of the parent metal.

In view of the comparatively high strength of flash welds, heat-treating after the welding operation does not improve the strength very much. Post weld heat treatment on welds in 61S, for example, increased the joint efficiency only about 20 per cent over that of the welds made in the T6 temper. The elongation, however, was greatly improved, reaching 80 per cent of the original T6 value. Higher strength alloys such as 24S and 75S show even less or no increase in strength if the heat treatment is performed after welding, but ductility is improved.

Welding the nonheat-treated tempers is sometimes advantageous, particularly with the high-strength alloys. A flash welding operation involves heavy forces during the final pushup in making the weld. The force that the machine must exert to do this depends on the yield strength of the sections being welded. Thus, it takes less pressure to weld material before heat treatment, since the yield strength is low. Post weld heat treatment would be required to attain maximum strength of both the weld and the parent material. Proper heat-treating temperature and time for the various alloys and tempers are shown in *Alcoa Aluminum and Its Alloys*.

Table 26 shows the result of tensile tests on flash welds in several alloys and tempers.

The resistance to corrosion of flash welds is essentially the same as that of welds made by other methods. Flash welded windows for all types of outdoor exposures have shown no preferential attack at the joints in many years' service.

Fatigue strengths of flash welds have been explored in only a few cases. Joints between aluminum and copper, for example, have shown a fatigue strength equal to that of the aluminum. The geometry of a flash welded joint—with its thin cast zone across the entire cross section—is good from the standpoint of uniform stress distribution. Consequently, they show good performance in fatigue loading.

An anodic finish on this type of joint shows less color contrast at the joint than is obtained on welds made by any other method. Where appearance after Alumilite finishing is an important factor, flash welds are the best joints that can be used.

Removing the flash of upset metal was a problem until the advent of the pinch-off die. Often the cost of dressing was nearly equal to the cost of making the weld. With a pinch-off die, it is frequently possible to produce an acceptable weld without further work.

Pinch-off dies have tool-steel knives attached to them. At push-up these knives cut almost completely through the flash.

Equipment—size, cost and special features

A flash welder is a precision tool, and its cost is from $5,000 to $100,000, depending on the size and controls. A 250 kva machine with upset forces of 30,000 pounds and a clamping force of 50,000 pounds should be capable of welding two square inches of 3S or one square inch of 61S. A machine of this type would cost $25,000 to $35,000.

In the process, the parts are clamped in electrodes and energized at from 5 to 20 volts depending on cross-sectional area. Contact is made by moving one or both platens, and current flows to establish an arc. When the joint interface is heated and melted, movement of the platen is accelerated to give a rapid push-up.

Flash-welding platen velocity usually ranges from 0.16 to 2.0 inches per second. Platen movement may be controlled mechanically, pneumatically or hydraulically. A mechanical control uses a linkage, a cam and a cam follower. The drive of the cam is controllable,

Aluminum and copper are flash welded together in making electrical fittings and connectors.

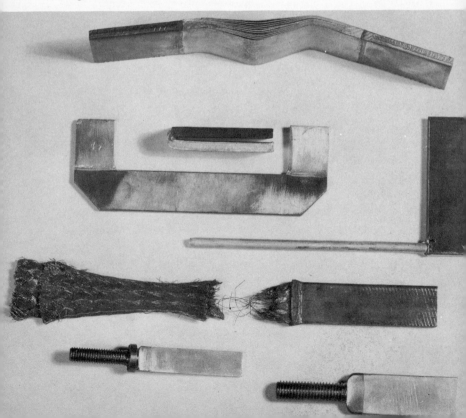

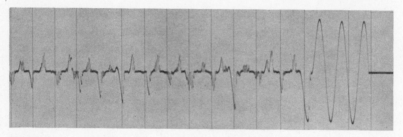

Fig. 4—An oscillogram showing flashing current and upset current for a typical flash weld.

and the cam shape may be changed. To move the platen on hydraulically operated machines, a valve is usually operated mechanically from a cam and cam follower, or—in more recent machines—a photo-electric cell controls a pressure pattern by following a curve or a cam.

Flashing currents are usually determined approximately with a current transformer and ammeter. An oscillogram, however, is the only accurate method of checking for continuity of flashing, or for rectification. See Fig. 4.

Rectification upsets electrical balance in the transformer. It is prevalent when joining dissimilar metals, such as copper and aluminum. According to estimates, current densities of 30,000 amperes per square inch are required at an average platen velocity of two inches per second. For most work, a flashing arc has practically unity power factor. Thus the power demand for this part of the operation is relatively low.

High and uniform upset velocity is the end point of a rapid acceleration. This is an important factor in making a good quality aluminum flash weld. Accelerations are hard to measure, hence velocities, distances and times are recorded. Upset velocities considered necessary for good joints between aluminum and aluminum range from 4 to 12 inches per second. Velocities desired for good joints between copper and aluminum are on the higher side of this scale. A good flash weld of copper to aluminum is shown in the photomicrograph in Fig. 5.

High upset velocities present a problem when the platen is massive. The platen is difficult to accelerate, and the energy of the moving mass deforms the joint when the energy of deceleration is absorbed by the weld. A recent development is to use a portion of this energy to shear off the upset metal, leaving a relatively smooth joint. This is the so-called "pinch-off" method of dressing welds.

Upset current flows momentarily after the weld is formed. Initial work on mechanical flash welders depended on a tapped transformer or tapped auto-transformer for adjustment of flashing current, and only the circuit impedance limited current at upset. Currents of 100,000 to 200,000 amperes per square inch were obtained. With currents of this magnitude, the time interval of current dwell becomes important. Controls are now available that can reduce the current to any desired value. This type of control increases the utility of the machine and is a desirable feature.

Upset current dwell time varies from one to ten cycles. It serves to assure that the parts are in solid contact and to insure that the weld zone stays molten and hot enough so that any oxides can be ejected by the upset force.

Fig. 5—An enlarged section of a copper-aluminum flash weld reveals the alloyed interfacial area which is about .00005 inch thick.

Flash welding electrodes, which act as clamps, the cooling water lines and a ring-shaped work piece are shown in this view.

Too long a dwell time may reduce the joint strength. For example, when using 100,000 amperes per square inch, the joint efficiencies of welds in the heat-treatable alloys drop after dwell time exceeds three cycles. Testing has shown that five cycles of dwell will drop the ultimate strength approximately 10 per cent.

Upset force is a function of the alloy and temper. The upset force may vary from 15,000 psi to 45,000 psi on the cross sectional area at the weld. The low-strength aluminum alloys and the annealed tempers are welded at lower pressures—the stronger alloys and heat-treated tempers at higher pressures.

Initial clamping distance or distance between dies is important. It varies with the section—whether it be a tube or a rod section. This dimension determines the distance from the arcing surface to the cold dies and thus the temperature gradient. Initial clamping distance is the sum of burn-off, upset distance, and final die opening. There is no fixed rule for determining these three distances,

Precise alignment and truly square miter joints are made by flash welding these extruded aluminum sections.

although the following relations have worked for thin-walled tubes and rods.

For thin-walled tubes, initial die opening should be 6 to 8 times the wall thickness. Upset distance will be in the order of 1.5 times the wall thickness. Final die spacing for such sections is usually from 0.7 to 1.0 times the wall thickness.

On the more concentrated massive sections like rods, initial clamping distance should be from 1.6 to 1.9 times diameter in upset distance, and final opening should be 0.5 diameter.

Clamping dies may be made from hard drawn copper if a limited number of pieces are to be fabricated. Copper-base material, RWMA Class 1 or Class 2, is better where a longer die life is required. Pinch-off dies are made entirely of air-quenching steel with a 50C Rockwell hardness.

Dies tend to wear on the edges, and sharply-defined contours become rounded. Hence, it is considered good practice to construct them so they may be "faced" where this is possible. Steel pinch-off dies must be resharpened after making 20,000 and 50,000 welds.

One of the requirements of flash welding that contributes to its success is good die alignment. This is essential for consistent weld strength. Axial alignment of the sections being welded should be adjusted and maintained so that the mating surfaces meet within 5 per cent of the minimum section thickness.

Dies cost between $400 and $2,000, depending on the shape and intricacy of the section. Sometimes it is possible to make a multiple-use die, particularly for developmental work where only a pilot number of specimens will be run.

Clamping force must be great enough so that the sections do not slip in the dies. Experience has shown it desirable to have at least twice the push-up force available for clamping. These forces should be readily and easily adjustable. On some sections, particularly those that are hollow or those that should not be deformed, it may be necessary to use a backup. Serrated dies are also used to prevent slippage.

Cooling the dies minimizes the amount of pick-up. Flash will not adhere as readily to a chilled die. It is more important to maintain die materials with poor heat conductivity, such as steel dies, at lower temperatures than dies of copper base alloys. Dies that are properly cooled will allow mass production rates of 60 to 300 welds per hour.

REFERENCES:

R. M. Curran and R. C. Becker, "The Flash Welding of Structural Aluminum Alloys," *Welding Research Council,* Volume XII, No. 11, November, 1947

P. M. Teanby, "A Review of Selected Papers on the Flash and Butt Welding of Light Alloy," British Welding Association, August, 1949, *Welding Research* Volume IV. Bound with *Transactions* of the Institute of Welding, Volume XIII, pp 16R–20R, February, 1950, London, England

E. F. Nippes, W. F. Savage, J. J. McCarthy and P. Patriarca, "Optimum Flash Welding Conditions for Aluminum Alloys," *Supplement to the Welding Journal,* October, 1950

Flash welding on aluminum aircraft gear retracting link assembly.

7

Metal Arc, Carbon Arc, and
Atomic Hydrogen Arc Welding

This section covers the three electric arc methods for welding aluminum that employ a flux to remove oxide as an essential part of the welding operation.

Metal arc welding

Welding aluminum by the metal arc process using a flux-coated electrode is a well-established procedure. Satisfactory results and economies have been achieved for many years. However, development of several types of gas-shielded arc welding methods has stimulated a shift in emphasis. Less coated electrode metal arc welding will be done as time goes on, and the trend is to electric arc methods that use no flux.

In metal arc welding, a heavy flux coating on the aluminum alloy electrode forms a gaseous envelope around the arc. In the weld puddle, it combines with aluminum oxides to form a slag. The slag, being lighter, floats to the surface and freezes. Deposited flux has to be at least partially removed after each bead is laid down in multipass welding.

This automatic carbon arc welding equipment has a motor-driven traverse arrangement lined up with a jig that clamps the cylindrical work pieces in place.

Penetration is excellent because of the concentrated heat generated by the electric arc. Joint preparation need not include beveled edges for stock under ¼ inch. Material up to ½ inch thick, if accessibility permits, can be welded from both sides with plain, square edges.

Welding procedures are conventional. Jig and tack weld the parts to assure correct alignment. Keep the arc about ⅛ to ³⁄₁₆ inch long to avoid excessive spatter. Reverse polarity (electrode positive) should be employed. Metal arc welding is done with a dc arc welding machine which can be either of the rectifier or rotating generator type. Approximate currents for various electrode diameters are shown in Table 27. Less heat will be required, and current values will be reduced correspondingly, if parts are preheated.

For fluidity when molten and for ductility during cooling, Alcoa 2S or Alcoa 43S electrodes are usually used. Electrode material can also be the same aluminum alloys as those being welded.

Metal arc welding is useful for welding all aluminum alloys. Because of the concentrated heat zone, cracking is minimized. Weld soundness and smoothness of the surface are not as good as other arc welding methods. The latter factors, and the necessity to use a welding flux, have been responsible for the decrease in popularity of this process.

Carbon arc welding

In a process much like gas welding, a carbon arc is used as a source of heat while filler metal is supplied from a separate coated rod. Adapted for automatic welding of long seams, this method employs bare filler wire with flux in powdered form that is fed into the arc along with the filler material.

The carbon arc affords a more concentrated heat source than a gas torch flame. Hence, it permits faster welding with less distortion. Soundness of welds is excellent and is comparable to that of good gas welding.

While this method met an important need during development of aluminum welding, its importance may be expected to decline. For those welding applications where a considerable amount of general heating can be tolerated, and where an easily finished bead is desired, gas welding is better. On the other hand, where minimum general heating, absence of flux, and very good properties in the weld are requirements, one of the types of inert gas shielded arc welding may well be selected. Another competing method, atomic hydrogen welding, has advantages similar to those of the carbon arc method.

Carbon arc welding may be expected to continue to fill certain needs, but not in the important place that it occupied during the development of aluminum welding.

Atomic hydrogen welding

Rapid welding of fairly thin aluminum sheet is the principal role of the atomic hydrogen method. This welding method may also be used for repairing aluminum castings. Machine settings are shown in Table 28, page 155.

One distinguishing difference between atomic hydrogen and other arc-welding methods is that the welding head or hand torch contains two tungsten electrodes, and the arc circuit is completely independent of the work. The tungsten electrodes are non-consumable.

A stream of hydrogen that passes through the ac arc is broken down from its H_2 gaseous state into individual hydrogen atoms. Energy to break the molecular bonds is furnished by the heat of the arc. As the stream blows toward the work, it cools. Then, hydrogen atoms recombine into gas molecules, and they give up heat energy. By this mechanism, they transfer a rather large amount of heat from the arc to the work. At the same time, oxygen is excluded.

Filler metal may be furnished, where required, by feeding a lightly fluxed rod into the molten pool. Presence of the gaseous envelop around the weld does not entirely preclude the need for flux, but very little is needed. Alcoa No. 22 gas-welding flux is painted on both sides of the joint, and the filler rod is dipped in flux. Residue of the used flux must be cleaned off after welding.

The same aluminum alloys are employed for filler rod as those recommended for gas welding (see Chapter 8). Often, a filler rod of the same alloy as the parent metal will work out best.

Welding brackets to the head of a process tank using the metal arc with a coated electrode.

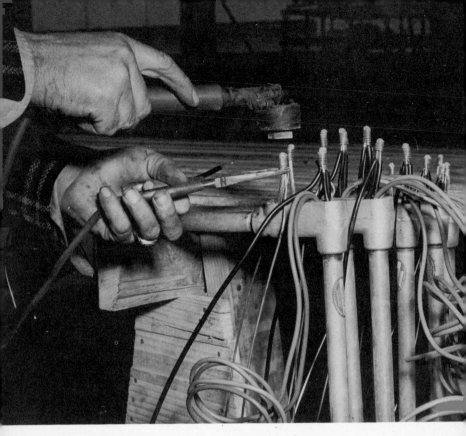

Carbon arc welding aluminum wire electrical connection.

No filler material is added on thin stock to weld corners or to make flanged butt welds. Using a flat backing strip of stainless steel, copper, carbon, or mild steel, well-fitted butt edges are welded either with or without added filler metal. Fillet welds always require filler metal to prevent undercutting.

The speed of atomic hydrogen welding is one of its chief virtues for welding aluminum. The pool of molten metal is clearly visible, so that an operator who is hand welding can see what he is doing. Because the arc is independent of the work, heat can be varied simply by moving the torch toward or away from the work. These factors, along with good control over metal flow, enable the operator to make sound welds that are well formed and neat in appearance without undue difficulty.

8

Gas Welding

Oxyacetylene and oxyhydrogen flames are both used in welding aluminum alloys. Natural gas and propane are also used. The oxyacetylene flame is used most widely because of its availability for welding other metals.

Use ordinary torches and equipment

Standard torches, hoses and regulators are suitable for welding aluminum. The data given in Table 29 on page 155 will serve as a guide to tip size as well as gas pressures. Details of the job, however, will modify these combinations. The skill of the operator will influence the selection of the tip; a fast worker can use a larger tip than a slower and less experienced worker.

The choice of filler material for gas welding is important. Commercially pure aluminum—Alcoa 2S—and metal of higher purity are generally welded with the same alloy as the parent metal. Alcoa 3S is also welded with 2S wire. A 43S filler rod is used for welding 52S, 61S, 62S or 63S alloys, when welding a combination of these alloys, or when welding these alloys to 2S or 3S. This rod, with substantially lower melting point than pure aluminum, tends to prevent shrinkage cracks by remaining partially molten after the adjacent metal has solidified.

Preheating the parts is recommended to avoid severe thermal strains in intricate castings and in sheet over ⅜-inch thick. Common practice is to preheat the part up to 800°F. Pyrometers are the most reliable way to determine temperature.

With experience, an operator can learn to use a gas or oil torch for local pre-heating. The flame is played just ahead of the welding torch so that the welding operator will not need to apply all the heat necessary to melt the metal with the welding torch.

Minimum distortion is obtained with edge or corner welds that permit the bead to be located on a crown or radius. Welded seams or fittings in flat areas should be avoided because of the shrinkage stresses they set up.

Cold packs in the form or water-soaked rags or carbon back-up blocks rarely serve any useful purpose in gas welding aluminum alloys. Higher flame settings to offset the cooling effect may cause more distortion than would occur without cold packs.

In gas welding, the following procedure should be employed: Align the parts accurately. Start with tack welds along the seam. Place the tack welds one or two inches apart on materials up to ¹⁄₁₆-inch thick. This spacing can be increased up to ten inches, for materials ½-inch thick or more. Adjust the torch to give a slightly reducing flame. Be sure the torch tip is clean and free of flux. Goggles should be removed while adjusting the torch flame.

Flux removes the oxide. The film of oxide formed on aluminum alloys combines with the flux at welding temperatures to form a slag. The slag comes to the surface of the weld leaving sound metal underneath. Alcoa No. 22 Welding Flux is recommended. Three parts are mixed with one part of tap water to form a paste, which is applied to the filler rod and to the joint.

Clean off the flux after welding. Any flux left on aluminum becomes a starting point for corrosion, and in the case of parts that are to be painted, this flux will loosen the paint over the welds. Where both sides of the weld are accessible, a part can be cleaned in a boiling water bath with a fiber brush. If the parts are too large

Gas welding is extensively used on food-handling vessels and utensils.

Locating welds near corners and tack welding joints carefully are valuable measures to prevent excessive buckling and distortion.

for tanks, scrub the joints with hot water and rinse with fresh water.

Closed vessels like beer barrels and airplane gasoline tanks are cleaned by immersion in acid solutions. There are a number of proprietary cleaning systems that are satisfactory for removing flux residue. In addition, the four cleaning systems shown below have been used in many production applications. Any one of these systems may be chosen.

Method No. 1—Nitric-hydrofluoric Cleaning.

(a) Immerse part for 3 to 5 minutes in cold acid.
1 gal. technical nitric acid (58–62% HNO_3) (39.5° Be)
½ pt. technical hydrofluoric acid (48% HF) (1.15 Sp. Gr.)
9 gal. water

(b) Water rinse—hot or cold

Method No. 2—Sulphuric Cleaning

(a) Immerse part for 10 to 15 minutes in cold acid or 4 to 6 minutes in acid held at 150°F
1 gal. technical sulphuric acid (93% H_2SO_4) (66° Be)
19 gal. water

(b) Water rinse—hot or cold

Method No. 3—Nitric Cleaning

(a) Immerse part for 5 to 10 minutes in cold acid.
1 gal. technical nitric acid (58–62% HNO_3) (39.5° Be)
1 gal. water

(b) Water rinse—hot or cold

Method No 4—Nitric-dichromate Cleaning

(a) Immerse part 5 to 10 minutes in cold acid.
1 pt. technical nitric acid (58–62% HNO_3) (39.5° Be)
14 oz. Sodium dichromate ($Na_2Cr_2O_7$)
1 gal. water

(b) Water rinse—cold or hot

Gas welding an aluminum jet aircraft component.

While all four methods are equally efficient for removing flux, Method No. 4 is applied only to parts that will not be used for handling food or allied products. The dichromate addition to the cleaning acid is effective as a means for preparing the surfaces to inhibit corrosion. It is used primarily for such applications as aircraft gasoline tanks.

To check the effectiveness of flux cleaning operations, place a few drops of water where the presence of flux is suspected. Collect this and drop it in a small tube containing a 5% silver nitrate solution. A white precipitate indicates the presence of flux.

Finishing methods for welds are the same as described on page 33.

80

9

Welding Aluminum
Alloy Castings

Before considering types of alloys and methods of welding used for aluminum castings, it is helpful to ask—why is the weld being made? Answers to this question tend to show three principal reasons for welding. On such a basis, three categories of welding aluminum castings can be set up.

They are: (1) foundry welding, (2) repair welding, and (3) assembly welding. Foundry welding is a regular routine in the production of sand castings. Small defects are corrected, metal for machining "clean-up" provided, minor design variations accomplished, etc. Repair welding, of course, is a means of restoring to service castings that have been broken or worn excessively. Assembly welding—joining cast pieces with other castings or wrought parts—is an important and successful manufacturing operation.

Foundry welding

Sand castings are commonly welded in the foundry. Permanent mold castings of aluminum can be welded, also, if desired. Aluminum die castings are not weldable for repair or alteration purposes.

The filler rod alloy employed is almost always identical to that of the casting itself. In fact, filler material can be cast in rod-shaped molds while production castings are being poured.

Preparation for welding starts with removal of all dross or unsound metal. Where an "as cast" surface is to be welded, wire brush it vigorously to take off any surface sand.

Choice of welding method is made on much the same basis as in other aluminum alloy welding. A considerable amount of successful work has been done with the inert gas tungsten arc. Gas, metal arc, carbon arc or atomic hydrogen welding can be used—usually with a furnace for general preheating.

After flaws have been repaired, areas built up, bosses added, or other necessary welds made, flux should be cleaned off if any was used.

Cast parts requiring heat treatment should, of course, be heat treated after welding.

If castings are to be impregnated to insure pressure-tightness, the impregnation must not be done until all welding is completed. Some caution should be exercised before impregnating a casting to make sure that it will not be likely to need any welding after impregnation.

Repair welding

Broken, eroded, or worn aluminum alloy sand and permanent mold castings are often repaired by welding.

Problems involved in making good welds on cast aluminum parallel those encountered with wrought metal.

Heat-treated casting alloys cannot be welded by any process without loss of mechanical properties. After welding, though, they can be heat treated again to restore their properties. If it is not practicable to heat treat after welding, and if the strength of the joint is important from design and service considerations, it may be well to test the repaired casting before using it.

Temperatures exceeding 400°F developed in the casting during preheating or welding will affect the mechanical properties of heat-treated aluminum alloy castings. In general, tensile properties will be lowered in the area immediately adjacent to the weld for all tempers because of the annealing effect of temperatures over 600°F. Areas heated in the range 400 to 600°F will usually suffer a loss in tensile strength and yield strength if in the -T6 condition, but will undergo little change in properties if in the -T7 or -T5 temper. A knowledge of the original heat treatment received by a casting is therefore essential in evaluating the effect of the welding operation on mechanical properties of the part.

Localized heating in the course of making a weld introduces temperature gradients and thermal strains in the casting. Cracks may develop during welding or during the contraction on cooling. To reduce the steepness of gradients between hot and cool areas, the entire casting is often preheated.

Even in preheating a complicated cast part, there may be trouble from temperature effects unless heating and cooling are carried out slowly and carefully. Specific practices depend on geometry of the individual part. Uniform temperature rise throughout a casting is sought by applying heat to the entire part with emphasis on any concentrated masses of metal.

Preventing cracks in or near the weld is easiest if the welding can be done by an arc welding method that concentrates the heat. Less widespread heating around the weld means less subsequent contraction. Another aid in avoiding cracks is the use of a filler alloy with good resistance to hot-short cracking combined with a low melting temperature. Alcoa 43S is the alloy usually chosen to give this combination of properties.

Permanent dimensional changes sometimes occur when parts are heated. This happens in all welding of aluminum. The only time it poses a serious problem, however, is in repair welding of broken or worn castings with machined surfaces. Repair welds can be made while keeping critical dimensions within precise tolerances, but this is a complicated matter. The only general rule that can be given is this: *Keep the heat of the welding concentrated.*

Preparation for welding a casting should begin with thorough cleaning. Oil, grease and dirt should be removed from the weld area with a suitable solvent. Oxide and adherent sand can be removed by wire brushing.

Tungsten arc welding has proved highly successful for foundry welding.

Chip out a 45-degree bevel on sections about 3/16 inch thick or heavier.

Where necessary, devise a clamp or jigging setup that will hold the parts in correct alignment. See that the casting is well supported, but make sure that clamps do not apply excessively high forces.

In general, no welding should be attempted if the casting has been impregnated. If an impregnated casting must be welded, the impregnating material can be partially removed by prolonged heating in the range of 300° to 400°F.

Flux the area of the weld unless an inert gas shielded arc is to be used for the actual welding.

Preheating the entire casting between 500° and 800°F is often helpful during repair welding. This can be done in a furnace or with gas torches. Sometimes both methods are combined. Do not permit overheating. Large castings may be distorted or may collapse completely if allowed to get too hot (above 900°F) in the course of preheating.

Welding technique for repair work by any method will involve a considerable amount of agitation of the molten pool—especially in thick sections. For repairing cracks, broken corners, etc., stir the molten pool with filler rod or a puddling iron to work dross and slag up to the surface of the weld.

Work in a small zone at one time. If the seam is a long one, make tack welds first to hold the parts in place.

For data on thicknesses, tip sizes, current settings, gas flow rates, and the like, refer to the section in this book that treats the welding method being employed.

If a considerable volume of new metal is required to repair a broken part, pouring the weld may be the easiest way to handle the job. A poured weld is essentially another casting poured into a shaped mold that includes the broken edges. Make the mold of clay, plaster of Paris, etc. so that it holds the parts in alignment and will produce the desired contour on the metal poured into it. Flux the edges that will be welded. Preheat to 900°–1100°F. Use molten 43 alloy filler or the same as in the casting, heated to 1300°F and not above 1350°F. When pouring and while the metal is freezing, use a puddling iron or a stiff wire brush to work oxide out of the weld.

It may be easier to make a separate cast insert to fill the hole. The sides of this piece should be chamfered to mate with the parent casting. The insert is first tack welded into place, and then the groove is filled by arc welding.

Assembly welding

There are few limitations to the use of welding as a production method for joining cast aluminum parts to each other or to wrought aluminum.

All kinds of castings except die castings can be spot welded or flash welded. Any welding method can be employed on aluminum sand or permanent mold castings.

Production cost advantages may be gained by combining cast and wrought aluminum pieces. Often, several parts welded together may take the place of an extremely elaborate casting or fabricated unit. There are other, similar cases when welded aluminum castings offer attractive possibilities in the light of limitations imposed by other approaches to the problem.

Flash welding of castings is not different in any significant respect from the same processes as used with wrought aluminum alloys. See Chapter 6.

Arc and gas welded castings may require some planning during the design stage for best results. No special considerations need be stressed in method or technique, except to note that 43S filler metal is most widely used where low production cost is the prime consideration. Other alloys are used for color match and to meet strength requirements.

Designs should anticipate the ordinary needs of welding. For example, accessibility will be a factor. Costs may be high if the weld is hard to reach.

Cast tabs or other kinds of locating points can be devised to save time in assembling parts precisely for welding.

Avoid welds between thick and thin sections. If thicknesses on both sides of the weld are approximately the same, and if the distances to masses of metal are about equal, it will be easy to bring both parts up to welding temperature at the same rate. This makes for faster operation and a better weld.

Stresses caused by contraction of cooling metal can be reduced by design choices. Locate the weld at or near a bend, if possible, or provide a shape that will allow some "give."

Joints made with flux should always be cleaned after welding, and they may be dressed down and finished by conventional methods if desired.

Tungsten arc welding a complicated aluminum alloy casting.

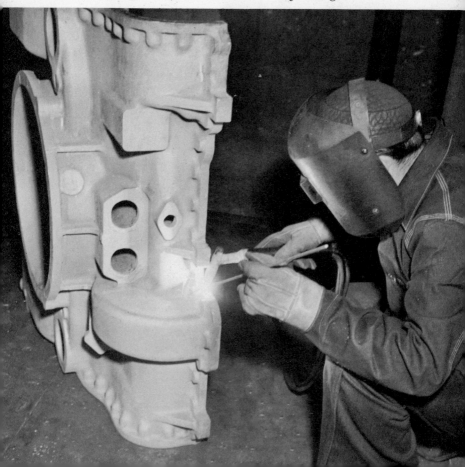

This is a hand-operated roller die set. It makes a pressure welded edge joint on two aluminum sheets and trims along the edge of the weld simultaneously.

10

Pressure Welding

Pressure welding promises to expand its field of application with further development. Although there are at present very few industrial uses for pressure welding in this country, much interest has been shown in its potential for sheet fabrication, electrical connections, joining thin sheets or foil, and for the joining of aluminum to other malleable metals.

Working the metal produces an effective joint

Where two clean, smooth metal surfaces are brought into intimate contact, a bond can be achieved. Pressure sufficient to decrease the cross-sectional area 50 to 75 per cent, applied by means of a standard mechanical or hydraulic press, or by roll-type dies, produces a permanent bond. It will be apparent from the magnitudes of deformation involved that the softer metals that deform most readily will give the most satisfactory pressure welds. Thus, joint efficiencies are greatest for the nonheat-treatable alloys in the annealed condition.

The theory is that when pressure is applied, the metallic surfaces are sealed off. Further pressure causes the metal to flow, exposing fresh metal. This pressure is sufficient to produce a weld in the true sense, with a continuous grain structure.

The pressure required to produce optimum reduction in cross-section varies with the gage, alloy and temper of the material. At room temperature, the range is from 50,000 to 200,000 psi. The pressure needed decreases as temperature is increased, but pressure welding is always accomplished at temperatures below the melting point of any of the alloy constituents.

All the nonheat-treatable aluminum alloys can be pressure welded in any of the standard tempers. In the -O temper, they have the

Here are several pressure welded aluminum samples. At the top, a socket is welded to .064-inch sheet using a ring-type die. In the center is a linear, roll-type weld between a rolled sheet and an extrusion. At the bottom is a punch-type pressure weld that was made with a hand tool.

best strength efficiency compared to the strength of the unwelded material.

Although heat-treated alloys can be pressure welded also, greatest joint strength is obtained if the welding is done in the annealed temper and the parts are heat treated afterward. The high-strength alloys give low joint efficiencies and may crack when pressure welded in the heat-treated tempers.

Clean surfaces are essential for good pressure welding. Chemical or solvent cleaning to remove oil or other foreign material is a necessary first step in preparing metal for welding. The preferred method for final cleaning that combines the necessary roughness with freedom from contamination is wire brushing by a rotary brush with .006-inch to .008-inch diameter stainless steel wire bristles. After brushing, there must be no contamination of the faying surfaces. However, if dust, dirt and moisture are excluded, a few hours—or even days—may elapse between cleaning and welding without adverse effects from re-formed oxide films.

Pressure welding dies must be of the greatest precision. Joint efficiency depends upon the accuracy with which pieces are brought together. In butt welding, for instance, absolutely no buckling, slipping or sliding is permissible.

Practical problems may be solved by pressure welding

At the present time, pressure welding is used for making lap welds in sheet and wire and butt welds in tube. Butt welds are also practicable in bar and wire stock.

Copper-aluminum joints have been made successfully, but deformations of 60 to 70 per cent are necessary to achieve optimum welds. Such joints in wire and bus bar have good electrical conductivity. Pressure welded joints on wire terminals or connecting parts may become a field of application. Further investigation will determine whether industrial applications of joints between dissimilar metals are useful.

Tools have been developed to form sheet into tube, to wire-brush the welding edges, to weld the edges between pressure rolls, and to shear off the surplus metal—in a continuous operation. This is a relatively high speed process with a reasonable tool cost and low fabrication costs. Possible fields of application of this technique include sheathing of electrical conductors, making down spouting, television and radio aerial tubes or other similar articles where the performance of pressure welded tube is adequate.

Other possible applications include welds for sealing metal packages, for floats of all kinds, and for condenser leads, studs, and handle connections. Very few of these fields have been explored.

Performance and strength of pressure welds

The strength of a pressure weld depends on the geometry of the section at the joint after the welding deformation has been applied. If the joint is made on tools that deform the metal by reducing the cross-section, a weakened joint will result. If, on the other hand, the deformation is applied by upsetting the metal, then the joint area is stiffened.

The simplest example of the first type is a lap joint in sheet, made with a tool that reduces the cross section about 70 per cent. Some cold work is introduced in making the weld. This increases yield strength locally at the joint. The decrease in cross-section more than offsets this strengthening, however. Starting with material in the annealed temper, the tensile breaking load across the joint is limited to about 80 per cent of the value in unwelded metal. Bending loads concentrate deflection in the reduced section at the joint, and the sharp groove presents a stress raiser that can affect the fatigue strength adversely. The use of such welds, then, depends on locating the joint normal to any bending loads and in areas where the loading is low. Locally stiffening of the parts by using cross members may be a useful expedient to carry such bending loads.

Upset pressure welds are exemplified by butt welds in wires. The ends of the wires are upset about 80 per cent of the diameter, so that a considerable increase in cross section is obtained. The breaking load in this case is equal to the strength of the unwelded wire for any temper that has sufficient ductility to stand the deformation without cracking. This is true for all the annealed tempers and is

Aluminum wire is lap welded by pressure in these dies. The wire joint at the right has been trimmed.

also true when the upset portion has been trimmed off to the diameter of the original wire. The performance of such welds in accelerated fatigue tests—for example, running over guides and pulleys—has been very good.

Pressure welds do a good job of holding liquid or gas pressures. While test vessels have been made in which the joints resisted leaking at pressures over 100 psi, applications in this field will probably be parts that must resist much lower pressures. Packages and cans, sheathing of cable to prevent moisture penetration, floats for gasoline or water, and other similar low-pressure applications present likely fields for development.

Resistance to Corrosion of pressure welds is as good as the parent metal. Since no fluxes, dissimilar metals as filler alloys or metallurgical changes from excessive welding heat are involved, the corrosion problem is reduced to determining the suitability of the parent alloy for the service intended. The practice of painting the faying surfaces or including a sealing material—sometimes used when making riveted or spot welded joints—is not possible when pressure welding.

93

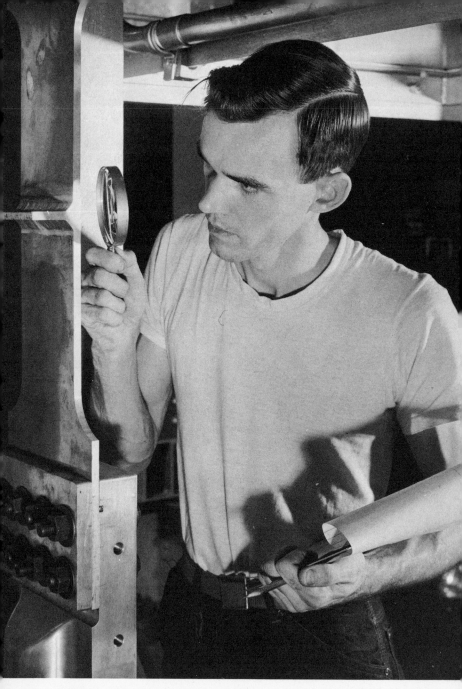

Alcoa's performance data are based on years of research and testing. This is a fatigue test specimen being examined for incipient cracks.

Performance of Aluminum Welds in Tests and Under Service Conditions

In the past, designers could count on sound, trouble-free welds only in soft-temper, low-strength aluminum alloys. The stronger alloys were welded, but tendencies toward brittleness and formation of cracks remained to be overcome.

Modern welding techniques—the inert gas shielded arc welding methods especially—have brought significant improvements in the performance that can be obtained in welds.

It should be observed at the outset, though, that many welds will not be critically stressed. Designs may be so arranged that the assembly will fail at some other location in case of an overload or mechanical abuse. Most of this section applies to those applications where the weld itself and adjacent metal are critical from the standpoint of strength. It is expected that these cases will become more common as designers take advantage of the cost-cutting opportunities to be gained with more reliable and more highly-stressed welds in aluminum alloys.

How welding affects strength

In nonheat-treatable alloys, the annealing effect at and near the weld takes away some of the strengthening imparted to the material by cold working.

In heat-treated aluminum alloys the heat of welding causes a change in the metallurgical structure. Thus, the mechanical properties of heat-treated aluminum alloys will partly revert to those of the annealed condition at and near the weld.

Limiting the heating effect to a smaller space is desirable. Arc welding methods are superior to gas welding in this respect.

Best performance can be expected from welds made with the inert gas shielded consumable electrode method and from resistance welding. Neither uses flux, and both apply a tremendous amount of heat right at the point of fusion for a minimum time interval. The extent of annealing on a cold worked or on a heat-treated structure is lessened. Also, benefits are derived in soundness and freedom from cracking when the heat is concentrated. Less metal around the weld has time to expand and contract thermally. Hence, the cracking tendency is reduced, and distortion of the welded assembly is lessened.

Heat treatment after welding may be feasible, depending on the shape and size of a welded part. Then, of course, to avoid heat treating twice, neither part would be heat treated before welding. Practical problems introduced by the geometry of the part or special features of the assembly may have to be solved to prevent excessive distortion during quenching.

Even though all welded parts and all filler metal may be of a heat-treatable alloy and properly treated, the designer should bear in mind that the weld bead is cast metal. Therefore, ductility in the weld bead itself will be lower than in the wrought parent metal.

If welding will involve two or more different heat-treatable alloys —to be heat treated as an assembly after welding—a complex problem is introduced. A compromise treatment may be needed to take into account the different characteristics involved. It would be well to get help from Aluminum Company of America when such a situation arises.

Locations and types of welds have an influence on performance. A butt weld, of course, transfers tension loads most efficiently. With full penetration,—whether welded from one or both sides—it presents a symmetry that makes for uniform stress distribution. It can

A guided bend test of a welded specimen at the Alcoa Process Development Laboratory.

be finished to the same thickness as adjacent stock. This prevents section changes that would concentrate stresses.

Fillet welds, on the other hand, always involve a corner of some sort. So do lap welds. Loading is usually a combination of shear with various magnitudes of tension and bending. Consequently, fillet and lap welds cannot be expected to perform in as high a stress range as butt welds, and they are loaded more conservatively.

In almost every design, it is possible to locate the seams and joining points in any one of several ways. Some locations will simplify forming the metal or the use of stock sizes. Others will make for easier accessibility during welding. Usually, these two are governing considerations. But, if highest strength is a major consideration, it may be advisable to choose weld locations that will subject joints to the lowest stresses in service.

97

Thus, welds might be placed near the neutral axis of a beam section—or near one end. Extra forming may make it feasible to avoid loading a fillet weld with highly concentrated stresses. Each individual case poses a separate problem and an individual opportunity in this respect.

Strength of butt and fillet welds

Numerous mechanical tests of weld strength have been made. Tables 30 and 31 summarize some of these results.

Yield strengths of welds are not given. The reason is that the actual yield strength usually varies from a low value in the heat-affected zone near the weld to a high value in unaffected parent metal. Hence, test results depend on the gage length employed in establishing the test stress-strain relationship. With any practical gage length, the numerical result is an average that has very little practical meaning.

Highest strength welds are obtained, as Table 30 shows, by using heat-treatable material and heat treating after welding. However, post-weld heat treatment entails some sacrifice in ductility as well as introducing the possibility of warping.

When welds are located in critical portions of a structure, the strength of the weld controls the strength of the assembly.

The width of the zone on each side of an arc weld that is affected by the welding heat depends on many variables; for example, the time and temperature of preheating, the number of weld passes, the temper of the parent metal, as well as the varying geometry that the designer must provide to meet the functional requirements of the parts. The width of the heat affected zone can be assumed to be $8\sqrt{t}$ on each side of a butt or fillet joint where t is the metal thickness. Beyond this width, the metal may be assumed to be unaffected by the heat of welding. This is an approximation based on the most unfavorable conditions but should be used unless a survey of the specific design being considered can be made.

The strength of butt welds in the alloys usually used for welding is shown in Table 30. The minimum tensile strength of the nonheat-treatable alloys is also shown. The latter value is usually chosen for design computations and is used as the basis of weld strength in the various codes governing safe design practices.

The strength of the welds in some heat-treatable alloys is also shown. Most frequently the parts are not heat-treated after the welding operation. For such applications, the values of tensile strength across the weld as shown in Table 30 can be used in designing joints with the application of appropriate factors of safety for the specific service. Checking design estimates by making destruction tests under conditions simulating service is a widely used practice when welding the heat-treatable alloys. The above applies also when post-weld heat-treatment can be done.

Fillet weld strengths are listed in Table 31 for various combinations of parent and filler metal. Unit strengths are expressed in terms of actual weld throat depth—not nominal weld size. Another point that should be noted is that both filler wire alloys and plate materials are significant. For example, if the same filler wire were used with a softer plate material, the shear strength may be appreciably less than indicated.

At the Alcoa Aluminum Research Laboratory, a wide variety of welded specimens are tested for their resistance to corrosion when they are intermittently immersed in a salt solution.

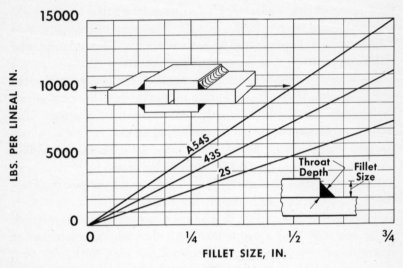

Fig. 6—*Transverse shear strength of fillet welds.*

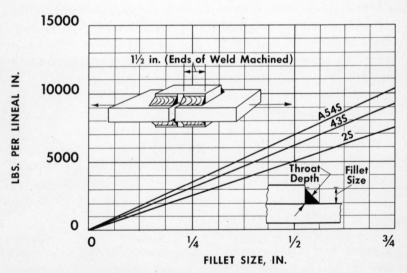

Fig. 7—*Longitudinal shear strength of fillet welds.*

Figs. 6 and 7 were made up to show transverse and longitudinal strengths of fillet welds as a function of weld size. Extrapolation from these curves to larger fillet sizes will not necessarily yield reliable data.

Resistance to impact should be considered from two viewpoints: resistance to permanent set and resistance to fracture.

The excellent performance of aluminum alloy parts—welded or not welded—in resisting permanent set under shock loading comes partly from aluminum's relatively low modulus of elasticity. The stress level induced by a given shock loading on a given design of member is lower for a low-modulus material. Yield strength plays an important part in resistance to permanent set, of course, and both factors, yield strength and modulus, must be taken into account.

If the stresses induced by shock loading exceed the yield strength of the material, then a permanent set will result, and resistance to fracture becomes increasingly important.

The resistance of an assembly to fracture depends mostly on the ductility of the material in the region of the highest stresses. A low-ductility material will fracture at a lower shock load than a high-ductility material. Behavior will also be influenced by the volume of metal that yields under the impact of the shock loading. Thus, an assembly that has a stress concentration at its weakest point will always give a poorer performance than one in which the high stresses are distributed over a fairly large area.

Tests of actual welded aluminum alloy assemblies under shock loads have demonstrated the following facts which may be useful in design:

1. It is often advisable to locate welds in low-stressed regions. The desirability of this depends to some extent on the strength and ductility of the weld in comparison with the surrounding metal.

2. Removal of weld beads has not been found generally beneficial in resistance to shock.

3. Severe localized shock loads can be applied immediately adjacent to butt welds without causing fracture of the weld itself, even though the parent metal may be permanently dented or even

fractured. Ductility of the weld plays an important part in determining the location of the fracture.

4. Generally speaking, welded assemblies of the softer alloys withstand shock loads more satisfactorily than those of harder alloys.

5. Welded assemblies, properly designed and fabricated, resist shock loading about as well as comparable riveted assemblies.

6. Welded assemblies, like other types of aluminum alloy construction, show no loss of impact resistance at low temperatures.

Fatigue strengths of welded structures follow the general rules that apply to other kinds of fabricated assemblies. The fatigue strength is governed by the peak stresses at points of stress concentration rather than by the nominal stresses. Anything that can be done to reduce the peak stresses by eliminating stress raisers will tend to increase the life of the assembly under repeated loads.

As would be deduced from the general principles of designing for repeated loads, the fatigue strength of a welded joint is dependent on the smoothness of the weld bead—sometimes to a greater extent than on the method of welding or the particular metal used in the weld bead or adjacent parts. Where a smooth weld bead is not achieved, the fatigue strength can be improved by machining the weld bead flush with the surface of the plate or by otherwise improving the smoothness of the bead. For welding processes that produce relatively smooth weld beads, there is little or no increase in strength with their removal. The benefit of smooth weld beads can be nullified by excessive spatter during welding. Spatter marks sometimes develop severe stress raisers in the parent metal adjacent to the weld.

The fatigue strength of welded butt joints in three aluminum alloys are shown in Fig. 8. For very large numbers of cycles, the fatigue strengths of the joints in the three alloys are practically equal. On the other hand, for small numbers of cycles the fatigue strengths are practically the same as the static strengths.

Generally speaking, welds in aluminum alloys perform very well under repeated load conditions. Tests have shown that properly designed and fabricated welded joints will generally perform as

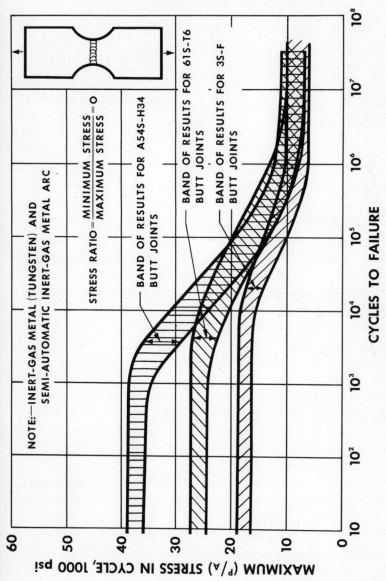

Fig. 8—Direct stress fatigue test results for welded aluminum.

The lightweight, strength and reliable weld performance of this aluminum alloy trailer body mean moving extra tons of payload every day.

well under repeated load conditions as will riveted joints designed for the same static loading.

The following rules have been found helpful in designing for long life:

1. Always give preference to simple, symmetrical joints that reduce secondary flexing to a minimum.

2. Where unsymmetrical joints are unavoidable, try to stiffen the joint in some way to reduce secondary flexing.

3. Always give preference to a butt joint over a lap joint.

4. Strive for smoothness. Avoid undercutting, cracks, excessive porosity, spatter, and other imperfections which might serve as stress raisers or starting points for cracks.

5. If smooth weld beads are not achieved at critical locations, consider machining or dressing the weld beads at such locations.

6. Use gradual changes in sections.

7. Don't add or attach secondary brackets, fittings, handles, bosses, and openings at locations of high stress.

Effect of temperature on the performance of welded joints

Aluminum alloys grow stronger and tougher at temperatures below room temperature. In general, they are somewhat weaker, as well as more ductile, at elevated temperatures. These characteristics also apply to welded joints in aluminum alloys.

Tests have shown that the strength of welds made with parent-metal filler material, in the nonheat-treatable alloys, at all temperatures from −320 to 700°F, is at least equal to that of the parent metal in the annealed condition at the same temperature.

For heat-treatable alloys, the effect of temperature cannot be stated quite so simply. In the case of 61S-T6 plate welded with 43S filler metal, for example, the strength of welded joints decreases with increasing temperature but at a lesser rate than does the strength of the parent material. At 500°F, the welded joint is as strong as the parent material. For 61S-T6 plates welded with 43S filler and heat treated and aged after welding, the strength of the welded joints decreases with increasing temperature at about the same rate as the strength of the parent material. Regardless of whether or not the 61S-T6 assembly is heat treated after welding, the strength increases at low temperatures, and the ductility remains about constant.

Resistance to corrosion
of welded aluminum assemblies

Many of the aluminum alloys can be welded without reducing the resistance of the assembly to corrosion. In general, the welding method does not influence resistance to corrosion.

Flux residues, of course, are corrosive. If the welding method employed requires flux, the geometry of the joint must permit thorough flux removal. Adequate procedures and checks must then be set up to assure that all flux is actually cleaned off. Procedures to do this are described in Chapter 8.

The environments considered here are atmospheric exposures, fresh waters and sea water, soils, and similar exposures. Problems that may arise in equipment for handling chemicals or process materials are likely to be complex. In such environments, minor differences of materials and techniques can result in greatly exaggerated performance differences.

Get the advice of specialists from Aluminum Company of America if you anticipate dealing with situations of this nature.

Nonheat-treatable alloys are not usually changed appreciably in resistance to corrosion by welding. Among the alloys that can be welded without much effect on their resistance to attack are 2S and alloys of higher purity, 3S, 4S, 50S, 52S, A54S, 61S, 62S, 63S, and cast alloys 43, 355 and 356. Welded combinations of these alloys also have good resistance to corrosion.

Heat-treatable alloys containing substantial amounts of copper, such as 14S, 17S and 24S, usually have their inherent resistance to corrosion lowered by welding. Along with their strength, most of their resistance can be restored if it is practicable to heat treat the assembly after welding. The resistance of 14S-T6, 24S-T6 and 24S-T8 (artificially aged) is less affected by welding than that of 14S-T4, 17S-T4 and 24S-T4 (naturally aged.) Painting serves to prevent attack as long as the paint coatings are adequately maintained and serviced.

Alclad aluminum alloys, as welded, show better resistance to corrosion than corresponding non-clad alloys welded in the same way. Both the core alloy and the exposed welded zone are electrochemically protected by the more anodic cladding. Typical alloys used are Alclad 3S and Alclad 4S. Although experience with Alclad 14S, Alclad 24S and Alclad 75S is limited, the same generality holds true for these heat-treatable alloys. Some exposure tests indicate that welding reduces the resistance of the latter three alloys to attack. Considerable improvement can be obtained by heat treating after welding.

Filler metal of commonly used alloys like 2S, 43S, A54S and 356 displays good inherent resistance to corrosion. High purity aluminum is often preferred for environments involving corrosive chemicals.

Aluminum-magnesium alloys used for filler material are highly resistant to corrosion. However, they tend to be anodic to most other aluminum alloys, and will thus be the sacrificial material in the event of galvanic corrosion. For this reason, they should be used with caution whenever the environment may subject the weld and parent metal to galvanic attack. Such situations as possible immersion in electrolytes should be considered.

Aluminum filler metals containing substantial amounts of copper

This is a twelve-foot section of a portable gin-pole for jobs like erecting power-line towers. It is rated at 6,000 pounds safe load capacity up to 60-foot assembled length, yet each portable section weighs only 100 pounds. Consumable electrode welding was used to assemble the triangular framework of 61S-T6 aluminum pipe.

are not as resistant to corrosion as the aluminum-magnesium alloys. They may produce stronger welds, however, and frequently resist corrosion adequately for common exposures. Most aluminum alloys are anodic to those containing copper, and parent metal of another alloy frequently protects copper-containing weld metal in the presence of an electrolyte.

The welding method employed can be said to result in only minor differences in resistance to corrosion of the weld and base metal. The inert gas shielded methods, as has been pointed out repeatedly, eliminate the potential hazard of incomplete flux removal.

Spot, seam and flash welding do not alter significantly the resistance to corrosion of such common aluminum alloys as 2S, 3S, 4S, 50S, 52S, A54S, 61S, 62S and 63S. Resistance welding of dissimilar alloys in this group has only minor effects.

Spot welds in Alclad 3S, Alclad 4S, Alclad 14S-T4, Alclad 14S-T6, Alclad 24S-T4, and Alclad 75S-T6 are electrochemically protected by the cladding on the sheet. This is true even if the weld nugget is so thick that it extends through to an outer metal surface. But, of course, better resistance to corrosion is experienced when the weld does not go through the outer cladding.

Resistance welds of 14S, 17S, 24S and 75S may be selectively attacked under severe or moderately severe conditions. This usually rules out spot welded construction with these alloys when corrosion is a factor. However, when the same alloys are spot welded to alclad parts of corresponding composition, the cladding electrochemically protects the non clad material at the faying surfaces. This improves over-all resistance to corrosion at the joint.

Increased resistance to corrosion may be obtained on a spot welded joint by welding through sealing compounds or sealing tape. High quality welds can be made through many sealing compounds, providing they are plastic at the time of welding. Recent developments indicate that a conducting tape may be used for sealing. Paints, any quick drying materials, or high-resistance fillers are not satisfactory because they give excessively high electrical resistance which cause poor welds or no welds at all.

12

Inspection and Quality Control

The basic purpose of inspection is less to find flaws than to insure uniformly high quality in the finished product. Consequently, the task of inspection begins with the selection of the right equipment, method, materials and personnel. These will make the greatest contribution to reducing the high cost of faulty work and excessive rejects.

Table 2 on Page 110 lists the causes of the common fusion weld defects so that corrective action can be taken. Welds in aluminum alloys are no different in this respect from welds in other metals.

Step-by-step visual inspection reveals many imperfections

Because it is simple, rapid and requires few instruments, visual inspection is one of the most valuable inspection methods. Many aspects of inspection are beyond the scope of visual examination. Correlation of visual examination with more exact findings revealed by other methods will considerably increase its usefulness.

The time to begin visual inspection is before welding. Edge preparation, cleaning, alignment and any flaws in the materials to be

Table **2**

Welding Defects and Their Causes

	Jigs	Sequence	Filler size	Technique	Heat	Manipulation	Cleaning	Flux
Dimensional defects								
Warpage	X	X						
Incorrect weld size			X	X		X		
Incorrect profile				X	X	X		
Overlap				X	X	X		
Excess concavity				X	X			
Excess convexity				X				
Structural discontinuities								
Porosity					X	X	X	
Nonmetallic inclusions				X			X	
Incomplete fusion				X	X	X	X	X
Inadequate penetration			X	X	X	X	X	
Undercutting			X	X	X	X		

welded can be detected then. Correcting them at this point will safeguard against rejection in the final stages of fabrication.

Inspection should continue throughout the welding process. The welding operator should be made responsible for checking to see that gas or current settings do not change. When several passes are to be made, he can check the previous pass before laying down the next one. This permits detection of slag accumulations that were not removed. He can spot cracks and remedy them when they are most accessible. Although the appearance of the weld is not a positive indication of quality, it gives a good clue to the care which has been used in making it. In spot welding, the operator checks the electrodes periodically for any change in dimensions or contour.

After the weld is completed, visual inspection reveals whether the weld bead is the right size. This is also the time to check the final appearance of the weld for such defects as spatter and roughness or cracks. In cases where standards have been established, the bead can now be inspected for extent, contour and continuity. A ten-power hand lens, fillet gages and workmanship standard samples can increase the reliability of the visual inspection.

When inspecting for flaws that bear on performance, the weld should be first cleaned of all flux and oxide coatings. Shot blasting and chipping should not be used until later, since they tend to smear over the defects such as cracks or fissures that are being sought.

Pressure testing or mechanical testing gives more positive results

Load testing reproduces, and in some cases exaggerates, the stresses a part will encounter in service.

Proof testing consists of applying, to a real part, a pressure or load approximating that which is expected in service without attaining values that would destroy the part.

Destructive testing gives a measure, based on actual failure, of the characteristics of joints and materials under consideration. It is useful in determining method, technique and materials to be used in fabricating parts to specifications. It can also be used to sample production. However, a sample can be better or worse than the assembly it is intended to represent, unless uniformity is maintained.

Obviously, it would be impractical to test all parts to destruction; therefore, proof testing gives a reliable index of the quality of each piece. When pressure tightness is under consideration, it is a fairly simple matter to make a hydrostatic test or an air test. When pressure testing, a margin of safety is usually established by making the test pressure $1\frac{1}{2}$ times the pressure anticipated in service. The load or pressure should not stress the part more than 75 per cent of the calculated yield strength.

Proof testing of mechanical components is less common than hydrostatic testing—mainly because of the requirements for elaborate testing equipment and special fixtures.

Metallographic inspection of fusion welds

Metallographic inspection affords a useful means of sampling the inner structure of welds without destroying the entire assembly. Grain structure, weld soundness, distribution of nonmetallic inclusions, and the extent and structure of the heat-affected region are all data that can be determined by metallographic inspection.

The weld may be sectioned with a core drill, trepan, or by sawing a cross section. After polishing, it is etched to make the structure more readily visible. It is then inspected by the naked eye, under low magnification, or under a microscope.

Much useful information can be obtained by simple polishing and finishing of a cross section with tools usually available in any shop. Filing to smooth a sawed surface, followed by another smoothing operation with No. 150 abrasive paper, will show the dimensions of the weld zone. Resistance welds as well as fusion welds are frequently inspected in this manner. Further definition of the weld zone may be obtained if the specimen is etched in a 5 per cent sodium hydroxide solution, followed by a nitric acid dip to remove the film that is formed by the etch.

This test can be relied on to determine weld penetration and the size of the weld and the presence of large voids or inclusions. It cannot be relied on to show other defects, for example, cracks, fine porosity, oxide inclusions or grain structure. Inspection for such defects requires a metallographic polishing operation by experienced personnel. The special skills required for polishing aluminum sections can be acquired by practice, and helpful instructions can be obtained by writing Aluminum Company of America.

The examination of the specimen for cracks or porosity can best be done without etching the specimen, particularly for small defects requiring a magnification of 100 X or more to be detectable. However, the structure of the weld and the transition zone is shown best if the specimen is etched.

The surfaces to be etched should be smoothed by filing or machining or by grinding on metallographic emery papers. With different alloys and tempers, the etching period will vary from a few seconds to several minutes and should be continued until the desired contrast is obtained. As a protection from the fumes liberated during the etching process, this work should be done under a hood. After etching, the specimens should be thoroughly rinsed and then dried with a blast of warm air. Coating the surface with a thin clear lacquer will preserve the appearance.

The following etching reagent is suggested for revealing the macrostructure:

1. For aluminum and aluminum-base alloys:

Hydrochloric acid (conc.)	3 parts
Hydrofluoric acid (48%)	2 parts
Water	17 parts

This solution is to be used at room temperature and etching is accomplished by either swabbing or immersing the specimen.

Radiographic examination is also a useful method for the inspection of welds. Examination of fusion welds reveals the distribution

A neat appearance usually means that the welding is sound.

and size of porosity in a weld structure. It also shows clearly lack of penetration and lack of fusion. In addition, most cracks are revealed satisfactorily on an X-ray film. In some cases, very fine cracks are present in the weld or transition zone which are so orientated that there are practically no changes in the resistance to penetration of X-rays, consequently such defects are not shown on a film. The X-ray therefore, cannot be relied upon to ascertain complete freedom from cracks. Bend tests or dye-penetrant tests are more searching methods for determining cracks.

There are two other defects that can occur in fusion welds of the aluminum alloys, namely, flux inclusions and oxide films. The density of such defects is substantially the same as that of aluminum and neither defect will give a clear indication on an X-ray film. In this case also, bend tests are a more reliable indication of the soundness of the weld structure.

The technique for operating X-ray equipment and for handling and processing X-ray film has been established and is available for general use. Communication with Aluminum Company of America is suggested if information on this phase is desired.

Gamma Ray examination of the weld structure is commonly performed on steel but is not useful for examining welds in the aluminum alloys. It is difficult to obtain sharp definitions of the defects on films made with gamma rays; consequently the method is seldom used.

Quality control of spot and seam welds

No economical, nondestructive method of inspecting all spot welds is available. Rigid control of machine settings, established welding procedure, the use of proper equipment, and qualified personnel are the best preventive measures against faulty welds. Electrical equipment is available to indicate any variations in welding current, force and time. Modern welder controls, if properly maintained, will insure proper control of the machine variables. The welder should be supplied by power lines free of wide voltage swings. Voltage regulation at the machine should be less than ±5 per cent. Where several machines are on one line, the voltage should not vary beyond these limits when several weld simultaneously.

Provide setup men with tables of proper machine settings. The success of any spot welding operation depends primarily on correct initial settings. These settings should be verified by frequent tests on materials of the same alloy and gage as the job being done. In the shop, these test samples may be examined by tearing the welded parts open and measuring the diameter of the weld buttons. See Fig. 9. If the weld button diameter is consistently greater than twice the thickness plus ⅟₁₆ inch, adequate weld strength is assured.

Further control may be had by conducting periodic shear tests on specimens welded at the same time as the production job. For example, welds in aircraft are welded and inspected by the procedure laid out in Specification Mil-W-626. A useful check can be made by sawing through the weld, smoothing with a file and a fine abrasive cloth, then etching with sodium hydroxide. Penetration between 20 and 80 per cent of the thickness is satisfactory, with 50 per cent the practical ideal. This test will determine weld penetra-

Fig. 9—Peel testing spot-welded pieces gives a quick indication of weld size and soundness.

tion and weld size, but is not reliable for detecting internal cracks and porosity.

Porosity and cracks can be detected by microscopic examination of properly etched and polished specimens. *The specimen is cut at the center of the weld zone and mounted for polishing. After the specimens are polished, they are etched in order to reveal the structure. Examination of specimens prepared by these methods will show the size, shape and location of the weld zone, and the

Checking the shear strength of a spot weld by a tensile test of the joint.

effects of the heat from the welding as well as the presence of porosity and cracks.

Radiography, used to detect cracks and porosity in some alloys, will determine the size and shape of the weld zone, thus providing a nondestructive method of inspection for these aspects of spot welds. Radiographic examination is expensive and is used primarily on aircraft quality work.

Qualified operators and controlled procedures offer the best assurance of good welding

To keep welding economical, a shop man or welding engineer has to keep the jobs moving. Interruptions for tests, inspection, etc. should be held to a minimum consistent with reliable work.

Experience has shown that a welding operator who has qualified to make good welds by a certain method can continue to do so. Of course, the work and equipment have to remain the same for this to be true.

Training and qualifying of operators under the code or standard that applies in each case should be done painstakingly. During the setup stages of a new job, rather extensive testing may be desirable. Then, during the production phase, all emphasis can be on uniformity of conditions, materials, appearances, equipment settings and procedures.

* 1. F. Keller and G. W. Wilcox, Polishing and Etching of Constituents of Aluminum Alloys," *Metal Progress,* April, 1933, Volume 23, p. 45.
   2. E. H. Dix, Jr., and F. Keller, "An Etching Reagent for Aluminum-Copper Alloys," *Mining and Metallurgy,* 1928, Volume 9, p. 327.
   3. F. Keller and R. A. Bossert, "Revealing the Microstructure of 24S Alloy," *Metal Progress,* 1942, Volume 41, pp. 63–72.
   4. K. R. Van Horn, "Radiography of Metals," *Metals Handbook,* 1948 Edition, pp. 141–145.
   5. F. Keller and D. W. Smith, "Correlation of Metallographic and Radiographic Examination of Spot Welds in Aluminum Alloys," *Welding Research Supplement to Welding Jnl.,* December, 1942, Volume 21, pp. 573s–583s.
   6. D. W. Smith and F. Keller, "Correlation of the Strength and Structure of Spot Welds in Aluminum Alloys," *Welding Research Supplement to Welding Jnl.,* January, 1944, Volume 23, pp. 23s–26s.
   7. Gerard H. Boss, "Radiographic Appraisal of Spot Welds in Aluminum," *Metal Progress,* April, 1948, Volume 53, pp. 522–527, 566.

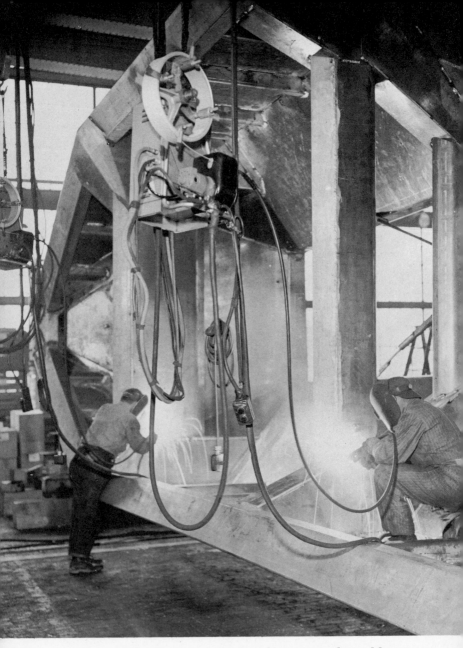

Welder controls and electrode feed mechanisms are elevated here to combine high welding speed with maximum safety.

13

Shop Safety Practices

Like most shop practices, safe welding of aluminum is largely a matter of common sense. With a few additions, the same rules of safety apply to welding aluminum as to welding any other metals.

Aluminum does not undergo any color changes when heated. It is necessary to remember or to sense by radiant heat that a certain piece is hot. There is no warning color. If skin burns do occur, they should be treated in accordance with standard medical practice. Aluminum burns are no different from those inflicted by other hot metals.

Oxygen, hydrogen and acetylene should be treated according to conventional safety practices. These gases are tapped from cylinders or pipe lines through regulating or reduction valves. Since the regulators work on the diaphragm principle, a tank valve should only be opened when the regulator diaphragm adjusting-screw is fully open. Otherwise, the full pressure of the gas may be blown against the diaphragm with enough force to break it.

Oil or grease must never be permitted around oxygen cylinders, regulators, valves or gages. Make sure that there is no oil or grease on your hands or gloves, or on the rags used around the welding equipment. Oil will ignite and burn violently in the presence of oxygen under pressure.

Valves and fittings for oxygen and many acetylene cylinders and pipe lines have right-hand threads; those for hydrogen have left-hand threads. This is a safety measure to prevent accidental interchange of regulators. It further avoids the possibility of mixed gases in regulators or lines.

Clamp, chain or otherwise secure the gas cylinders so that there is no chance of their tipping. Open flames should be kept away from cylinders and hoses. Electrical circuits, particularly arc-welding leads, should also be kept away from gas cylinders and hoses.

Provide ventilation in enclosed areas

Fresh air in the form of a forced draft is essential for welders working on the interior of tanks or other enclosed vessels. Arcs and flames reduce the supply of available oxygen, and the combustion products create an additional hazard. If fresh air is supplied to the welding operator in such a way as to sweep the fumes away, this hazard is minimized. Furthermore, the man can work faster.

Welding gasoline or chemical tanks, or any tankage that has been used, should not be undertaken until the parts have been steam cleaned. Removal of contamination is essential to reduce the danger of explosion and pollution. See 1952 Safe Practices A6.0-52 issued by the American Welding Society for the recommended procedures.

Similarly, if a solvent is used to clean the parts before welding, make sure that it is completely removed before proceeding. Most solvents are flammable and some produce harmful gases when heated or burned.

Another fume problem is created by the use of fluxes. When aluminum fluxes are melted, the fumes may be unpleasant and slightly irritating. Inhalation should therefore be avoided. Gas welding in the usual shop atmosphere—not in an enclosed vessel—results in concentrations that are slight, and no special ventilation is required. However, metal-arc welding or carbon-arc welding produces a substantially greater quantity of such fumes, usually requiring forced exhaust to outdoors. These fumes contain particles of flux that should not be inhaled. Incidentally, the deposition or condensation of fumes on steel structures will eventually cause rusting.

When handling packages of flux, take care that a minimum of dust

Operation	Shade number
Inert gas shielded tungsten electrode	12–14
Inert gas shielded consumable electrode	12–14
Atomic hydrogen	11–12
Metal arc	10–11
Carbon arc	10–11
Gas welding	5– 6
Gas welding helpers	3– 4

is raised. This dust is as harmful as the fumes given off during welding. Instruct men to wash their hands after handling flux and keep lunches away from areas where flux powders are stored or mixed.

Protect your eyes—and those of other people

Practically all welding operations require eye protection—to eliminate glare from fusion-welding operations—or to avoid burns from metal that is expelled in the resistance-welding process. Goggles should therefore be worn by operators and other personnel who find it necessary to be in the vicinity. When no glare is created, clear goggles of standard design are satisfactory.

Standard goggle shades are suitable for glare elimination. Though requirements will vary among individuals, Table 3 gives suggested shades for a variety of production work.

Inert gas shielded welding creates a relatively clear, ray-transmitting atmosphere in the immediate vicinity of the arc. Consequently, radiation is greater and a darker shade of protective filter glass is needed. For the same reason, be sure that the operator's skin is well protected. Although there is less danger from hot metal or slag spatter, the greater radiation can cause a painful "sunburn" on exposed skin.

Electrical shock can be a hazard if cables and other insulated equipment are allowed to deteriorate. Replace damaged cable. Don't use cracked electrode holders or guns. Keeping equipment in shape is important with the arc welding methods that employ cooling water. Moisture—and possible leaks—increase the danger of shock.

14

Tables

Physical Properties of Alcoa Wrought Alloys

ALCOA ALLOY NO.	Approx weight (Lb/cu in.)	Electrical conductivity, (% of Int. annealed copper standard)	Thermal conductivity at 25°C (cgs units) [1]	Approximate melting range (Degrees F)	Relative resistance to corrosion [2]	Relative Suitability for Welding [3]						
						Gas	Arc with flux	Arc with inert gas	Resistance welding	Pressure welding	Brazing	Soldering
D1S-O	0.098	62	0.56	1195–1215	A	A	A	A	B	A	A	A
D1S-H14	0.098	62	0.56	1195–1215	A	A	A	A	A	A	A	A
EC-0	0.098	62	0.56	1195–1215	A	A	A	A	B	A	A	A
EC-H19	0.098	62	0.56	1195–1215	A	A	A	A	A	A	A	A
2S-O	0.098	59	0.53	1190–1215	A	A	A	A	B	A	A	A
2S-H18	0.098	57	0.52	1190–1215	A	A	A	A	A	A	A	A
3S-O	0.099	50	0.46	1190–1210	A	A	A	A	B	A	A	A
3S-H18	0.099	40	0.37	1190–1210	A	A	A	A	A	A	A	A
Alclad 3S-O	0.099	..	..	..	A	A	A	A	B	A	A	A
Alclad 3S-H18	0.099	..	..	..	A	A	A	A	A	A	A	A
4S-O	0.098	42	0.39	1165–1205	A	A	A	A	B	A	B	B
4S-H38	0.098	42	0.39	1165–1205	A	B	A	A	A	B	B	B
11S-T3	0.102	36	0.34	995–1190	C	D	D	D	D	D	D	D
11S-T8	0.102	..	..	995–1190	C	D	D	D	D	D	D	D
14S-T4	0.101	34	0.32	950–1180	C	D	B	B	B	C	D	D
14S-T6	0.101	40	0.37	950–1180	C	D	B	B	B	D	D	D
Alclad 14S-T3	0.101	..	..	..	A	D	B	B	B	C	D	D
Alclad 14S-T6	0.101	..	..	..	A	D	B	B	B	C	D	D
17S-T4	0.101	30	0.29	955–1185	C	D	B	B	A	D	D	D
18S-T61	0.102	40	0.37	945–1180	C	D	B	B	B	D	D	D
24S-T3	0.100	30	0.29	935–1180	C	D	B	B	B	C	D	D
24S-T36	0.100	30	0.29	935–1180	C	D	B	B	B	C	D	D
Alclad 24S-T3	0.099	..	..	..	A	D	B	B	B	C	D	D
Alclad 24S-T36	0.099	..	..	..	A	D	B	B	B	C	D	D
32S-T6	0.097	35	0.33	990–1060	C	D	B	B	C	C	D	D
50S-O	0.097	50	0.46	1160–1205	A	A	A	A	B	A	B	B
50S-H38	0.097	50	0.46	1160–1205	A	A	A	A	A	B	B	B
A51S-T6	0.098	45	0.41	1025–1200	B	A	A	A	A	C	B	B
J51S-O	0.097	56	0.51	1143–1210	A	A	A	A	B	A	A	A
J51S-T6	0.097	58	0.52	1143–1210	A	A	A	A	C	A	A	A
52S-O	0.097	35	0.33	1100–1200	A	A	A	A	B	A	C	C
52S-H38	0.097	35	0.33	1100–1200	A	A	A	A	A	B	C	C
53S-T4	0.097	40	0.37	1075–1205	A	A	A	A	A	C	A	B
53S-T6	0.097	40	0.37	1075–1205	A	A	A	A	A	C	A	B
A54S-O	0.096	32	0.30	1095–1190	A	C	A	A	B	A	D	D
A54S-H34	0.096	32	0.30	1095–1190	A	C	A	A	B	C	D	D
A54S-H38	0.096	32	0.30	1095–1190	A	C	A	A	A	C	D	D
56S-O	0.095	29	0.28	1055–1180	A	C	A	A	B	A	D	D
56S-H38	0.095	27	0.26	1055–1180	A	C	A	A	A	C	D	D
61S-T4	0.098	40	0.37	1080–1205	A	A	A	A	A	C	A	B
61S-T6	0.098	40	0.37	1080–1205	A	A	A	A	A	C	A	B
62S-T4	0.098	45	0.41	1080–1205	A	A	A	A	A	C	A	B
62S-T6	0.098	45	0.41	1080–1205	A	A	A	A	A	C	A	B
63S-T5	0.098	53	0.50	1140–1205	A	A	A	A	A	C	A	B
75S-T6	0.101	30	0.29	890–1180	C	D	D	D	B	D	D	D
Alclad 75S-T6	0.101	..	..	..	A	D	D	D	B	D	D	D

[1][2][3] See footnotes page 126.

Table **4**

Ultimate tensile strength (lbs/sq in.)	Yield strength tension (lbs/sq in.) [6]	Elongation (% in 2 in.)		Shear strength (lbs/sq in.) [7]	Fatigue strength (lbs/sq in.) [8]	Brinell hardness (500-kg. load, 10-mm ball.)	ALCOA ALLOY NUMBER
		Sheet specimen (1/16 in. thick)	Round specimen (1/2 in. diam.)				
10,000	4,000	43	..	7,000	3,000	19	DD1S-0
14,000	13,000	12	..	9,000	5,000	26	DD1S-H14
12,000	4,000	..	[9]	8,000	..	..	EC-0
27,000	24,000	..	[10]	15,000	7,000	..	EC-H19
13,000	5,000	35	45	9,000	5,000	23	2S-0
24,000	22,000	5	15	13,000	9,000	44	2S-H18
16,000	6,000	30	40	11,000	7,000	28	3S-0
29,000	27,000	4	10	16,000	10,000	55	3S-H18
16,000	6,000	30	40	11,000	..	..	Alclad 3S-0
29,000	27,000	4	10	16,000	..	..	Alclad 3S-H18
26,000	10,000	20	25	16,000	14,000	45	4S-0
41,000	36,000	5	6	21,000	16,000	77	4S-H38
55,000	43,000	..	15	32,000	18,000	95	11S-T3
59,000	45,000	..	12	35,000	18,000	100	11S-T8
62,000	42,000	..	20	38,000	20,000	105	14S-T4
70,000	60,000	..	13	42,000	18,000	135	14S-T6
63,000	40,000	20	..	37,000	..	..	Alclad 14S-T3
68,000	60,000	10	..	41,000	..	..	Alclad 14S-T6
62,000	40,000	..	22	38,000	18,000	105	17S-T4
61,000	46,000	..	12	39,000	17,000	120	18S-T61
70,000	50,000	18	..	41,000	20,000	120	24S-T3
72,000	57,000	13	..	42,000	18,000	130	24S-T36
65,000	45,000	18	..	40,000	..	..	Alclad 24S-T3
67,000	53,000	11	..	41,000	..	..	Alclad 24S-T36
55,000	46,000	..	9	38,000	16,000	120	32S-T6
21,000	8,000	24	..	15,000	12,000	36	50S-0
32,000	29,000	6	..	20,000	14,000	63	50S-H38
48,000	43,000	..	17	32,000	11,000	100	A51S-T6
16,000	7,000	29	..	..	..	..	J51S-0
..	..	..	..	..	..	..	J51S-T6
28,000	13,000	25	30	18,000	17,000	45	52S-0
42,000	37,000	7	8	24,000	19,000	85	52S-H38
30,000	20,000	..	21	18,000	13,000	62	53S-T4
37,000	32,000	..	13	23,000	13,000	80	53S-T6
34,000	15,000	27	..	21,000	17,000	58	A54S-0
40,000	33,000	13	..	24,000	19,000	73	A54S-H34
45,000	39,000	10	..	27,000	21,000	..	A54S-H38
42,000	22,000	..	35	26,000	20,000	65	56S-0
60,000	50,000	..	15	32,000	22,000	100	56S-H38
35,000	21,000	22	25	24,000	14,000	65	61S-T4
45,000	40,000	12	17	30,000	14,000	95	61S-T6
35,000	21,000	..	25	24,000	14,000	65	62S-T4
45,000	40,000	..	17	30,000	14,000	95	62S-T6
27,000	21,000	12	..	17,000	10,000	60	63S-T5
83,000	73,000	11	11	48,000	23,000	150	75S-T6
76,000	67,000	11	..	46,000	..	..	Alclad 75S-T6

Typical Mechanical Properties [4][5]

[4][5][6][7][8][9][10] See footnotes page 126.

①Multiply listed value by .81 to change it into Btu/second/sq ft/in./°F.

②Corrosion resistance ratings A, B, C and D are relative ratings in decreasing order of merit. An "A" rating is highest. However, under many conditions alloys rated "D" are used with entirely satisfactory results. On the other hand, alloys rated "A" require protection in some exposures.

③Weldability ratings A, B, C and D are relative ratings defined as follows:
A. Generally weldable by all commercial procedures and methods.
B. Weldable with special technique or on specific applications which justify preliminary trials or testing to develop welding procedure and weld performance.
C. Limited weldability because of crack sensitivity or loss in resistance to corrosion and mechanical properties.
D. No commonly used welding methods have so far been developed.

④For all Alcoa alloys, wrought and cast, the following data apply:
(a) Young's modulus of elasticity may be taken as 10,300,000 psi: (b) Modulus of rigidity may be taken as 3,800,000 psi; (c) Poisson's ratio is 0.33; (d) Bearing strength is equal to 1.8 times the tensile strength, provided the edge distance, in the direction of stressing, is not less than twice the diameter of the hole.

⑤Mechanical properties are obtained on ASTM specimens. Since minimum guaranteed values vary with the commodity, they are not given in this table.

⑥Yield strength is the stress at which the material exhibits a permanent set of 0.2 per cent.

⑦Shearing strengths are single-shear values obtained from double-shear tests.

⑧Fatigue endurance values are based on withstanding 500 million cycles of completely reversed stress using the R. R. Moore type of machine and specimen.

⑨EC-O wire will have an elongation of approximately 23% in 10 inches.

⑩EC-H19 wire will have an elongation of approximately 1½% in 10 inches.

Nominal Composition of Wrought Alloys

Table **5**

Alloy[1]	Per Cent of Alloying Elements—Aluminum and Normal Impurities Constitute Remainder								
	Copper	Silicon	Manganese	Magnesium	Zinc	Nickel	Chromium	Lead	Bismuth
EC	99.45% minimum Aluminum								
2S	99% minimum Aluminum								
3S[2]	...	...	1.2	...	...	...	...	...	...
4S[2]	...	...	1.2	1.0	...	...	...	...	...
11S	5.5	...	...	...	...	...	...	0.5	0.5
14S[2]	4.4	0.8	0.8	0.4	...	...	...	...	...
17S	4.0	...	0.5	0.5	...	...	...	...	...
18S	4.0	...	...	0.6	...	2.0	...	...	...
B18S	4.0	...	...	1.5	...	2.0	...	...	...
24S[2]	4.5	...	0.6	1.5	...	...	...	...	...
32S	0.9	12.2	...	1.1	...	0.9	...	...	...
43S	...	5.0	...	...	...	...	...	...	...
50S	...	...	...	1.2	...	...	...	...	...
J51S	0.25	0.35	...	0.6	...	...	...	...	...
A51S	...	1.0	...	0.6	...	...	0.25	...	...
52S	...	...	...	2.5	...	...	0.25	...	...
53S	...	0.7	...	1.3	...	...	0.25	...	...
A54S	...	...	...	3.5	...	...	0.25	...	...
56S	...	...	0.1	5.2	...	...	0.1	...	...
61S	0.25	0.6	...	1.0	...	...	0.25	...	...
62S	0.25	0.6	...	1.0	...	...	...	...	...
63S	...	0.4	...	0.7	...	...	...	...	...
72S	...	...	...	...	1.0	...	...	...	...
75S[2]	1.6	...	...	2.5	5.6	...	0.3	...	...

[1] Heat-treatment symbols have been omitted since composition does not vary for different heat-treatment practices.

[2] The Alclad form of these alloys consist of a "core" of the basis alloy coated with pure aluminum or a suitable alloy.

Physical Properties of Alcoa Casting Alloys

ALCOA ALLOY NO.	Approx. weight (lb/cu in.)	Electrical conductivity, annealed (% of int. copper std.)	Thermal conductivity at 25°C (CGS units) [1]	Approximate melting range (Degrees F)	Relative resistance to corrosion [2]	Relative Suitability for Welding [3]						
						Gas	Arc with flux	Arc with inert gas	Resistance	Pressure	Brazing	Soldering
SAND-CASTING ALLOYS												
43-F	0.097	37	0.34	1065–1170	B	A	A	A	A	D	C	D
108-F	0.101	31	0.29	970–1160	D	B	B	B	B	D	D	D
113-F	0.106	30	0.29	965–1160	D	C	C	C	C	D	D	C
122-T61	0.107	33	0.31	965–1155	D	C	C	C	C	D	D	D
142-T571	0.102	34	0.32	990–1175	C	C	C	C	C	D	D	D
142-T77	0.102	38	0.35	990–1175	C	C	C	C	C	D	D	D
195-T4	0.102	35	0.33	970–1190	C	C	C	C	C	D	D	D
195-T6	0.101	33	0.31	970–1190	C	C	C	C	C	D	D	D
212-F	0.104	30	0.29	965–1160	D	C	C	C	C	D	D	D
214-F	0.096	35	0.33	1110–1185	A	C	C	C	C	D	D	D
B214-F	0.096	38	0.35	1090–1170	A	C	B	B	C	D	D	D
F214-F	0.096	36	0.34	1090–1185	A	C	B	B	C	D	D	D
220-T4	0.093	21	0.21	840–1120	A	D	D	D	D	D	D	D
319-F	0.101	27	0.26	960–1120	D	B	B	B	B	D	D	D
319-T5	0.101	..	...	960–1120	D	B	B	B	B	D	D	D
319-T6	0.102	..	...	960–1120	C	B	B	B	B	D	D	D
355-T51	0.098	43	0.40	1015–1150	B	B	B	B	B	D	C	D
355-T6	0.098	36	0.34	1015–1150	B	B	B	B	B	D	C	D
355-T71	0.098	..	...	1015–1150	B	B	B	B	B	D	C	D
356-T51	0.097	43	0.40	1035–1135	B	B	B	B	B	D	C	D
356-T6	0.097	39	0.36	1035–1135	B	B	B	B	B	D	C	D
356-T71	0.097	..	...	1035–1135	B	B	B	B	B	D	C	D
A612-F	0.102	35	0.33	1105–1195	B	C	C	C	C	D	A	C
PERMANENT-MOLD CASTING ALLOYS												
43-F	0.097	37	0.34	1065–1170	B	A	A	A	A	D	C	D
A108-F	0.101	37	0.34	970–1135	D	B	B	B	B	D	D	D
113-F	0.106	30	0.29	965–1160	D	C	C	C	C	D	D	C
C113-F	0.106	27	0.26	970–1145	D	C	C	C	C	D	D	C
122-T551	0.107	..	...	965–1155	D	C	C	C	C	D	D	D
122-T65	0.107	..	...	965–1155	D	C	C	C	C	D	D	D
A132-T551	0.098	29	0.28	1000–1050	C	B	B	B	B	D	D	D
D132-T5	0.100	26	0.25	970–1080	C	B	B	B	B	D	D	D
138-F	0.107	25	0.24	945–1110	D	C	C	C	C	D	D	D
142-T571	0.102	34	0.32	990–1175	C	C	C	C	C	D	D	D
142-T61	0.102	33	0.31	990–1175	C	C	C	C	C	D	D	D
B195-T4	0.101	33	0.31	970–1170	C	C	C	C	C	D	D	D
B195-T6	0.101	33	0.31	970–1170	C	C	C	C	C	D	D	D
A214-F	0.097	34	0.32	1075–1180	A	C	B	B	C	D	D	D
333-F	0.100	26	0.25	960–1085	C	C	C	C	C	D	D	D
333-T5	0.100	29	0.28	960–1085	C	C	C	C	C	D	D	D
333-T6	0.100	29	0.28	960–1085	C	C	C	C	C	D	D	D
355-T51	0.098	43	0.40	1015–1150	B	B	B	B	B	D	C	D
355-T6	0.098	36	0.34	1015–1150	B	B	B	B	B	D	C	D
355-T71	0.098	..	...	1015–1150	B	B	B	B	B	D	C	D
356-T6	0.097	39	0.36	1035–1135	B	B	B	B	B	D	C	D
356-T7	0.097	40	0.37	1035–1135	B	B	B	B	B	D	C	D
C612-F	0.103	40	0.37	1120–1190	B	C	C	C	C	C	A	C
750-T5	0.104	..	...	435–1200	D	D	D	D	B	D	A	D

[1][2][3] See footnotes page 130.

Table 6

		Typical Mechanical Properties ④⑤					
		Elongation (% in 2 in.)					
Ultimate tensile strength (lbs/sq in.)	Yield strength, tension (lbs/sq in.) ⑥	Sheet specimen (1/16 in. thick)	Round specimen (1/2 in. diam.)	Shear strength (lbs/sq in.) ⑦	Fatigue strength (lbs/sq in.) ⑧	Brinell hardness (500 kg load, 10-mm. ball)	ALCOA ALLOY NO.
SAND-CASTING ALLOYS							
19,000	8,000	..	8.0	14,000	8,000	40	43-F
21,000	14,000	..	2.5	17,000	11,000	55	108-F
24,000	15,000	..	1.5	20,000	9,000	70	113-F
41,000	40,000	..	⑨	32,000	8,500	115	122-T61
32,000	30,000	..	0.5	26,000	...	85	142-T571
30,000	23,000	..	2.0	24,000	10,500	75	142-T77
32,000	16,000	..	8.5	26,000	7,000	60	195-T4④⑩
36,000	24,000	..	5.0	30,000	7,500	75	195-T6
23,000	14,000	..	2.0	20,000	9,000	65	212-F
25,000	12,000	..	9.0	20,000	7,000	50	214-F
20,000	13,000	..	2.0	17,000	...	50	B214-F
21,000	12,000	..	3.0	17,000	...	50	F214-F
48,000	26,000	..	16.0	33,000	8,000	75	220-T4
27,000	18,000	..	2.0	22,000	10,000	70	319-F
30,000	26,000	..	1.5	24,000	...	80	319-T5
36,000	24,000	..	2.0	29,000	10,000	80	319-T6
28,000	23,000	..	1.5	22,000	7,000	65	355-T51
35,000	25,000	..	3.0	28,000	9,000	80	355-T6
35,000	29,000	..	1.5	26,000	10,000	75	355-T71
25,000	20,000	..	2.0	20,000	7,500	60	356-T51
33,000	24,000	..	3.5	26,000	8,500	70	356-T6
28,000	21,000	..	3.5	20,000	...	60	356-T71
35,000⑪	25,000⑪	..	5.0⑪	...	8,000	75⑪	A612-F
PERMANENT-MOLD CASTING ALLOYS							
23,000	9,000	..	10.0	16,000	...	45	43-F
28,000	16,000	..	2.0	22,000	...	70	A108-F
28,000	19,000	..	2.0	22,000	9,500	70	113-F
30,000	24,000	..	1.5	24,000	9,500	85	C113-F
37,000	35,000	..	⑨	30,000	8,500	115	122-T551
48,000	36,000	..	⑨	36,000	9,000	140	122-T65
36,000	28,000	..	0.5	28,000	13,500	105	A132-T551
36,000	28,000	..	1.0	28,000	13,500	105	D132-T5
30,000	24,000	..	1.5	24,000	...	100	138-F
40,000	34,000	..	1.0	30,000	10,500	105	142-T571
47,000	42,000	..	0.5	35,000	9,500	110	142-T61
37,000	19,000	..	9.0	30,000	9,500	75	B195-T4④⑩
40,000	26,000	..	5.0	32,000	10,000	90	B195-T6
27,000	16,000	..	7.0	22,000	...	60	A214-F
34,000	19,000	..	2.0	27,000	14,500	90	333-F
34,000	25,000	..	1.0	27,000	12,000	100	333-T5
42,000	30,000	..	1.5	33,000	15,000	105	333-T6
30,000	24,000	..	2.0	24,000	...	75	355-T51
42,000	27,000	..	4.0	34,000	10,000	90	355-T6
36,000	31,000	..	3.0	27,000	10,000	85	355-T71
38,000	27,000	..	5.0	32,000	13,000	85	356-T6
32,000	24,000	..	6.0	25,000	11,000	70	356-T7
35,000⑪	18,000⑪	..	8.0⑪	...	11,000	70⑪	C612-F
23,000	8,500	..	10.0	13,000	9,000	45	750-T5

④⑤⑥⑦⑧⑨⑩⑪ See footnotes page 130.

① Multiply listed value by 0.81 to change it into Btu/second/sq ft/in./°F.

② Corrosion resistance ratings A, B, C and D are relative ratings in decreasing order of merit. An "A" rating is highest. However, under many conditions alloys rated "D" are used with entirely satisfactory results. On the other hand, alloys rated "A" require protection in some exposures.

③ Weldability ratings A, B, C and D are relative ratings defined as follows:
   A. Generally weldable by all commercial procedures and methods.
   B. Weldable with special technique or on specific applications which justify preliminary trials or testing to develop welding procedure and weld performance.
   C. Limited weldability because of crack sensitivity or loss in resistance to corrosion and mechanical properties.
   D. No commonly used welding methods have so far been developed.

④ For all Alcoa alloys, wrought and cast, the following data apply:
   (a) Young's modulus of elasticity may be taken as 10,300,000 psi; (b) Modulus of rigidity may be taken as 3,800,000 psi; (c) Poisson's ratio is 0.33; (d) Bearing strength is equal to 1.8 times the tensile strength, provided the edge distance, in the direction of stressing, is not less than twice the diameter of the hole.

⑤ Mechanical properties are obtained on ASTM specimens. Since minimum guaranteed values vary with the commodity, they are not given in this table.

⑥ Yield strength is the stress at which the material exhibits a permanent set of 0.2 per cent.

⑦ Shearing strengths are single-shear values obtained from double-shear tests.

⑧ Fatigue endurance values are based on withstanding 500 million cycles of completely reversed stress using the R. R. Moore type of machine and specimen.

⑨ Less than 0.5 per cent.

⑩ On standing at room temperature for several weeks, the properties will approach those of the -T6 temper.

⑪ From tests made approximately 30 days after casting.

Nominal Composition of Casting Alloys

Table 7

Alloy[1]	Per Cent of Alloying Elements—Aluminum and Normal Impurities Constitute Remainder					
	Copper	Silicon	Magnesium	Zinc	Nickel	Tin
SAND-CASTING ALLOYS						
43	. . .	5.0	. . .	. . .	. . .	. . .
108	4.0	3.0	. . .	. . .	. . .	. . .
112	7.0	. . .	. . .	1.7	. . .	. . .
113	7.0	2.0	. . .	1.7	. . .	. . .
122	10.0	. . .	0.2	. . .	. . .	. . .
142	4.0	. . .	1.5	. . .	2.0	. . .
195	4.5	0.8	. . .	. . .	. . .	. . .
212	8.0	1.2	. . .	. . .	. . .	. . .
214	. . .	. . .	3.8	. . .	. . .	. . .
B214	. . .	1.8	3.8	. . .	. . .	. . .
F214	. . .	0.5	3.8	. . .	. . .	. . .
220	. . .	. . .	10.0	. . .	. . .	. . .
319	3.5	6.3	. . .	. . .	. . .	. . .
355	1.3	5.0	0.5	. . .	. . .	. . .
356	. . .	7.0	0.3	. . .	. . .	. . .
A612	0.5	. . .	0.7	6.5	. . .	. . .
PERMANENT-MOLD CASTING ALLOYS						
43	. . .	5.0	. . .	. . .	. . .	. . .
A108	4.5	5.5	. . .	. . .	. . .	. . .
113	7.0	2.0	. . .	. . .	. . .	. . .
C113	7.0	3.5	. . .	. . .	. . .	. . .
122	10.0	. . .	0.2	. . .	. . .	. . .
A132	0.8	12.0	1.2	. . .	2.5	. . .
D132	3.5	9.0	0.8	. . .	0.8	. . .
138	10.0	4.0	0.3	. . .	. . .	. . .
142	4.0	. . .	1.5	. . .	2.0	. . .
B195	4.5	2.5	. . .	. . .	. . .	. . .
A214	. . .	. . .	3.8	1.8	. . .	. . .
333	3.8	9.0	. . .	. . .	. . .	. . .
355	1.3	5.0	0.5	. . .	. . .	. . .
356	. . .	7.0	0.3	. . .	. . .	. . .
C612	0.5	. . .	0.35	6.5	. . .	. . .
750	1.0	. . .	. . .	. . .	1.0	6.5

[1]Heat-treatment symbols have been omitted since composition does not vary for different heat-treatment practices.

Butt Welds—Tungsten Arc
Approximate Welding Conditions

Stock thickness, inch	Preparation (See facing page)	Position	Current, amperes a-c	Dia. of tungsten, inch	Gas cup dia., inch	Argon gas flow, CFH	Filler rod dia., inch	Preheat, °F	Number of passes	Wire consumption, lb/100 ft.
$\frac{1}{16}$		Flat	70	$\frac{1}{16}$	$\frac{3}{8}$	20	$\frac{3}{32}$	None	1	$\frac{1}{2}$
		Horiz. & Vert.	70	$\frac{1}{16}$	$\frac{3}{8}$	20	$\frac{3}{32}$	None	1	$\frac{1}{2}$
		Overhead	60	$\frac{1}{16}$	$\frac{3}{8}$	25	$\frac{3}{32}$	None	1	$\frac{1}{2}$
$\frac{1}{8}$		Flat	125	$\frac{1}{8}$	$\frac{7}{16}$	20	$\frac{1}{8}$	None	1	2
		Horiz. & Vert.	115	$\frac{3}{32}$	$\frac{3}{8}$	20	$\frac{1}{8}$	None	1	2
		Overhead	120	$\frac{3}{32}$	$\frac{3}{8}$	25	$\frac{1}{8}$	None	1	2
$\frac{3}{16}$	A	Flat	175	$\frac{1}{8}$	$\frac{7}{16}$	25	$\frac{5}{32}$	None	2	$4\frac{1}{2}$
	B	Horiz. & Vert.	160	$\frac{1}{8}$	$\frac{7}{16}$	25	$\frac{5}{32}$	None	2	$4\frac{1}{2}$
	C	Overhead	170	$\frac{1}{8}$	$\frac{7}{16}$	30	$\frac{5}{32}$	None	2	5
$\frac{1}{4}$	A	Flat	225	$\frac{3}{16}$	$\frac{1}{2}$	30	$\frac{3}{16}$	Optional	2	8
	B	Horiz. & Vert.	200	$\frac{5}{32}$	$\frac{1}{2}$	30	$\frac{3}{16}$	Optional	2	8
	C	Overhead	215	$\frac{3}{16}$	$\frac{1}{2}$	35	$\frac{3}{16}$	Optional	2	10
$\frac{3}{8}$	A	Flat	325	$\frac{1}{4}$	$\frac{5}{8}$	35	$\frac{3}{16}$	Up to 400	2	$15\frac{1}{2}$
	B	Horiz. & Vert.	250	$\frac{3}{16}$	$\frac{5}{8}$	35	$\frac{3}{16}$	Up to 600	3	22
	C	Overhead	275	$\frac{3}{16}$	$\frac{5}{8}$	40	$\frac{3}{16}$	Up to 600	3	32
	D	Flat	360	$\frac{1}{4}$	$\frac{5}{8}$	35	$\frac{3}{16}$	Up to 400	2	14
	E	Horiz. & Vert. Overhead	260	$\frac{3}{16}$	$\frac{5}{8}$	35	$\frac{3}{16}$	Up to 600	2	14
	F	Flat	325	$\frac{1}{4}$	$\frac{5}{8}$	35	$\frac{3}{16}$	Up to 400	3	$15\frac{1}{2}$
	G	Horiz. & Vert.	250	$\frac{3}{16}$	$\frac{5}{8}$	35	$\frac{3}{16}$	Up to 600	4	$15\frac{1}{2}$
	H	Overhead	275	$\frac{3}{16}$	$\frac{5}{8}$	40	$\frac{3}{16}$	Up to 600	3	32
$\frac{1}{2}$	A	Flat	350	$\frac{1}{4}$	$\frac{5}{8}$	35	$\frac{3}{16}$	Up to 600	3	30
	B	Horiz. & Vert.	260	$\frac{3}{16}$	$\frac{5}{8}$	35	$\frac{3}{16}$	Up to 600	3	43
	C	Overhead	280	$\frac{1}{4}$	$\frac{5}{8}$	40	$\frac{3}{16}$	Up to 600	4	55
	D	Flat	400	$\frac{1}{4}$	$\frac{5}{8}$	35	$\frac{3}{16}$	Up to 600	3	30
	E	Horiz. & Vert. Overhead	270	$\frac{3}{16}$	$\frac{5}{8}$	35	$\frac{3}{16}$	Up to 600	3	30
	F	Flat	350	$\frac{1}{4}$	$\frac{5}{8}$	35	$\frac{3}{16}$	Up to 600	4	30
	G	Horiz. & Vert.	260	$\frac{3}{16}$	$\frac{5}{8}$	35	$\frac{3}{16}$	Up to 600	4	30
	H	Overhead	280	$\frac{1}{4}$	$\frac{5}{8}$	40	$\frac{3}{16}$	Up to 600	4	55

Table **8**

Edge Preparation

Stock thickness, inch	Flat	Horizontal and Vertical	Overhead
1/16 and 1/8	0 to 1/8	0 to 1/8 ... 0 to 1/8	0 to 1/8
3/16	60° ... 0 to 3/16 ... 1/16 **A**	60° ... 90° **B**	0 to 3/16 ... 1/16 ... 110° **C**
to	90° ... 0 to 3/16 ... 1/16 **D**	90° ... 90° **E**	
1/2	60° ... 0 to 3/16 ... 1/16 ... 1/4 x 1 1/2 min. ... 3/4 ... 3/32 **F**	90° ... 60° **G**	1/16 ... 3/4 ... 3/32 ... 0 to 3/16 ... 110° **H**

133

Edge Welds—Tungsten Arc
Approximate Welding Conditions

Stock thickness, inch	Position	Current amperes a c	Dia. of tungsten, inch	Gas cup dia., inch	Argon gas flow, CFH	Filler rod, dia., inch	Preheat °F	Number of passes	Wire consumption, lb/100 ft.
1/16	Flat	55	1/16	3/8	20	3/32	None	1	3/4
	Horiz. & Vert.	55	1/16	3/8	20	3/32	None	1	3/4
	Overhead	55	1/16	3/8	25	3/32	None	1	3/4
1/8	Flat	110	3/32	3/8	20	1/8	None	1	4
	Horiz. & Vert.	100	3/32	3/8	20	1/8	None	1	4
	Overhead	100	3/32	3/8	25	1/8	None	1	4
3/16	Flat	150	1/8	7/16	25	5/32	None	1	8
	Horiz. & Vert.	150	1/8	7/16	25	5/32	None	1	8
	Overhead	160	1/8	7/16	30	5/32	None	1	8
1/4	Flat	200	5/32	1/2	30	5/32	Optional	1	15
	Horiz. & Vert.	190	5/32	1/2	30	5/32	Optional	1	15
	Overhead	200	5/32	1/2	35	5/32	Optional	1	15
3/8	Flat	270	3/16	5/8	35	3/16	Optional	1	33
	Horiz. & Vert.	230	3/16	5/8	35	3/16	Optional	2	33
	Overhead	250	3/16	5/8	40	3/16	Optional	3	33
1/2	Flat	275	3/16	5/8	35	3/16	Optional	3	60
	Horiz. & Vert.	240	3/16	5/8	35	3/16	Optional	3	60
	Overhead	260	3/16	5/8	40	3/16	Optional	3	60

Table 9

Edge Preparation

Stock thickness, inch	Flat	Horizontal and Vertical	Overhead
1/16 to 3/16			
1/4 to 1/2			

135

Table **10**

Fillet Welds—Tungsten Arc

Edge Preparation

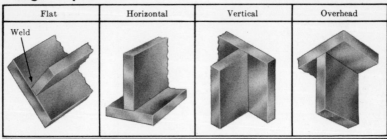

Flat	Horizontal	Vertical	Overhead

Approximate Welding Conditions

Stock thickness, inch	Position	Current, amperes a c	Dia. of tungsten, inch	Gas cup dia., inch	Argon gas flow, CFH	Filler rod dia., inch	Preheat, °F	Number of passes	Wire consumption, lb/100 ft.
1/16	Flat	80	1/16	3/8	20	3/32	None	1	1/2
	Horiz. & Vert.	80	1/16	3/8	20	3/32	None	1	1/2
	Overhead	70	1/16	3/8	25	3/32	None	1	1/2
1/8	Flat	150	1/8	7/16	20	1/8	None	1	2
	Horiz. & Vert.	120	3/32	3/8	20	1/8	None	1	2
	Overhead	135	3/32	3/8	25	1/8	None	1	2
3/16	Flat	215	5/32	1/2	25	5/32	None	1	4 1/2
	Horiz. & Vert.	180	1/8	7/16	25	5/32	None	1	4 1/2
	Overhead	190	5/32	7/16	30	5/32	None	1	4 1/2
1/4	Flat	260	3/16	1/2	30	3/16	Optional	1	7
	Horiz. & Vert.	235	3/16	1/2	30	3/16	Optional	1	7
	Overhead	240	3/16	1/2	35	3/16	Optional	1	7
3/8	Flat	345	1/4	5/8	35	3/16	Up to 400	2	17
	Horiz. & Vert.	290	3/16	5/8	35	3/16	Up to 600	2	17
	Overhead	290	3/16	5/8	40	3/16	Up to 600	3	17
1/2	Flat	375	1/4	5/8	35	3/16	Up to 600	3	30
	Horiz. & Vert.	300	1/4	5/8	35	3/16	Up to 600	3	30
	Overhead	310	1/4	5/8	40	3/16	Up to 600	3	30

Table 11

Corner Welds—Tungsten Arc
Edge Preparation

Flat	Horizontal	Vertical	Overhead

Approximate Welding Conditions

Stock thickness, inch	Position	Current, amperes a c	Dia. of tungsten, inch	Gas cup dia., inch	Argon gas flow, CFH	Filler rod dia., inch	Preheat, °F	Number of passes	Wire consumption, lb/100 ft.
$\frac{1}{16}$	Flat	60	$\frac{1}{16}$	$\frac{3}{8}$	20	$\frac{3}{32}$	None	1	$\frac{1}{2}$
	Horiz. & Vert.	60	$\frac{1}{16}$	$\frac{3}{8}$	20	$\frac{3}{32}$	None	1	$\frac{1}{2}$
	Overhead	60	$\frac{1}{16}$	$\frac{3}{8}$	25	$\frac{3}{32}$	None	1	$\frac{1}{2}$
$\frac{1}{8}$	Flat	115	$\frac{1}{8}$	$\frac{3}{8}$	20	$\frac{1}{8}$	None	1	2
	Horiz. & Vert.	115	$\frac{3}{32}$	$\frac{3}{8}$	20	$\frac{1}{8}$	None	1	2
	Overhead	115	$\frac{3}{32}$	$\frac{3}{8}$	25	$\frac{1}{8}$	None	1	2
$\frac{3}{16}$	Flat	160	$\frac{1}{8}$	$\frac{7}{16}$	25	$\frac{5}{32}$	None	1	$4\frac{1}{2}$
	Horiz. & Vert.	160	$\frac{1}{8}$	$\frac{7}{16}$	25	$\frac{5}{32}$	None	1	$4\frac{1}{2}$
	Overhead	170	$\frac{1}{8}$	$\frac{7}{16}$	30	$\frac{5}{32}$	None	1	$4\frac{1}{2}$
$\frac{1}{4}$	Flat	210	$\frac{5}{32}$	$\frac{1}{2}$	30	$\frac{3}{16}$	Optional	2	7
	Horiz. & Vert.	200	$\frac{5}{32}$	$\frac{1}{2}$	30	$\frac{3}{16}$	Optional	1	7
	Overhead	215	$\frac{3}{16}$	$\frac{1}{2}$	35	$\frac{3}{16}$	Optional	1	7
$\frac{3}{8}$	Flat	280	$\frac{3}{16}$	$\frac{5}{8}$	35	$\frac{3}{16}$	Optional	2	17
	Horiz. & Vert.	250	$\frac{3}{16}$	$\frac{5}{8}$	35	$\frac{3}{16}$	Optional	2	17
	Overhead	260	$\frac{3}{16}$	$\frac{5}{8}$	40	$\frac{3}{16}$	Optional	3	17
$\frac{1}{2}$	Flat	290	$\frac{3}{16}$	$\frac{5}{8}$	35	$\frac{3}{16}$	Optional	3	30
	Horiz. & Vert.	260	$\frac{3}{16}$	$\frac{5}{8}$	35	$\frac{3}{16}$	Optional	3	30
	Overhead	280	$\frac{3}{16}$	$\frac{5}{8}$	40	$\frac{3}{16}$	Optional	3	30

Pipe Welding—Tungsten Arc
Approximate Welding Conditions

Nominal pipe size, inch—Schedule 40	Position	Backup	Preheat, °F	Current, amperes a c	Dia. of tungsten, inch	Argon flow, CFH	Filler rod dia., inch	Number of passes	Wire consumption, lb/100 joints
1	Horizontal (rolled)	Optional	None	130	$3/32$	25	$1/8$	1	1
	Horizontal (fixed)	Yes	None	120	$3/32$	25	$1/8$	1	1
	Vertical	Optional	None	125	$3/32$	25	$1/8$	1	1
2	Horizontal (rolled)	Optional	None	150	$1/8$	25	$1/8$	2	$3\frac{1}{2}$
	Horizontal (fixed)	Yes	None	130	$1/8$	25	$1/8$	2	5
	Vertical	Optional	None	140	$1/8$	25	$1/8$	2	$3\frac{1}{2}$
3	Horizontal (rolled)	Optional	Optional	190	$5/32$	25	$5/32$	2	6
	Horizontal (fixed)	Yes	Up to 400	150	$5/32$	30	$5/32$	2	12
	Vertical	Optional	Optional	170	$5/32$	25	$5/32$	2	6
4	Horizontal (rolled)	Optional	Optional	225	$5/32$	30	$3/16$	2	12
	Horizontal (fixed)	Yes	Up to 400	175	$5/32$	35	$5/32$	2	18
	Vertical	Optional	Optional	200	$5/32$	30	$5/32$	3	12
6	Horizontal (rolled)	Optional	Optional	250	$3/16$	30	$3/16$	2	22
	Horizontal (fixed)	Yes	Up to 600	190	$3/16$	40	$3/16$	2	36
	Vertical	Optional	Optional	220	$3/16$	35	$3/16$	3	22
8	Horizontal (rolled)	Optional	Optional	275	$3/16$	35	$3/16$	3	38
	Horizontal (fixed)	Yes	Up to 600	225	$3/16$	45	$3/16$	3	60
	Vertical	Optional	Up to 600	250	$3/16$	40	$3/16$	4	38
12	Horizontal (rolled)	Optional	Optional	325	$1/4$	40	$3/16$	3	75
	Horizontal (fixed)	Yes	Up to 600	250	$3/16$	50	$3/16$	4	120
	Vertical	Optional	Up to 600	300	$3/16$	45	$3/16$	6	75

Edge Preparation

Nominal pipe size, inch—Schedule 40	Horizontal	Vertical
1 to 1½	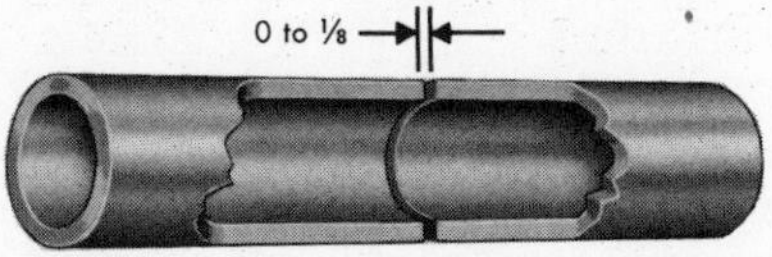 0 to ⅛ (rolled)	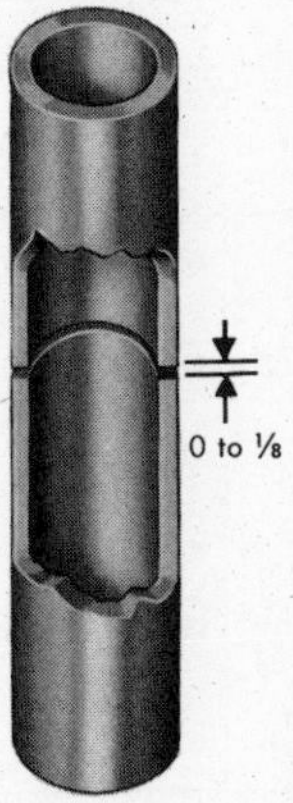 0 to ⅛
	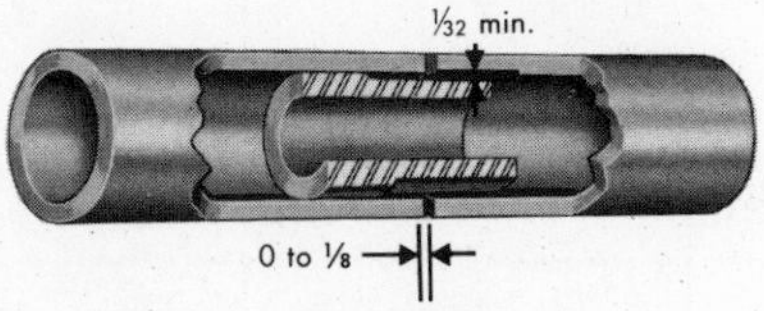 1/32 min. 0 to ⅛ (fixed)	
2 to 12	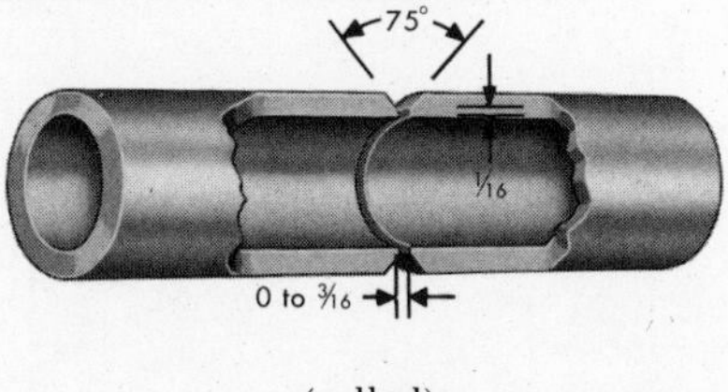 75° 1/16 0 to 3/16 (rolled)	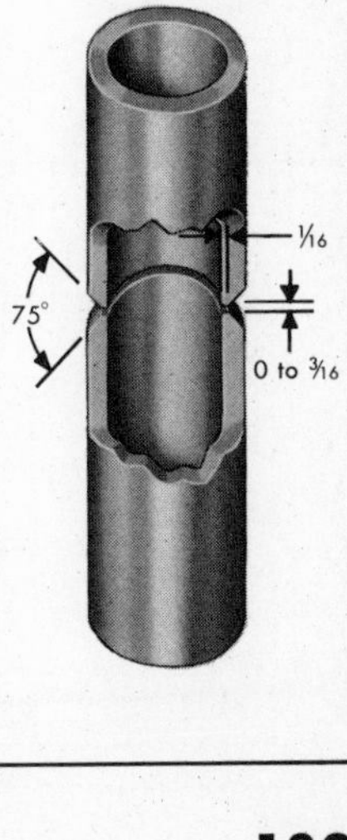 1/16 75° 0 to 3/16
	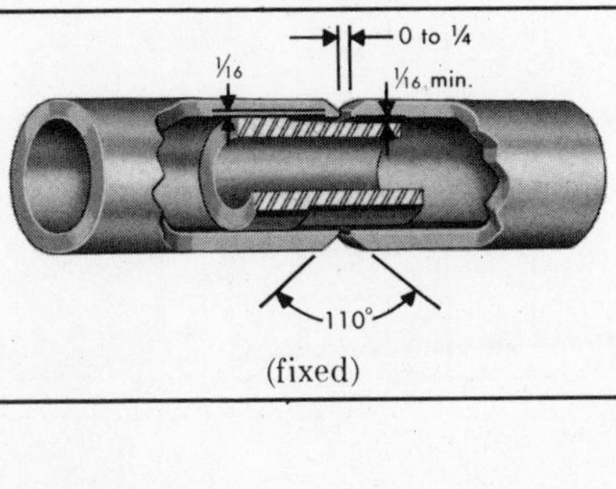 0 to ¼ 1/16 1/16 min. 110° (fixed)	

Butt Welds—⅛″—⅜″
Inert Gas—Consumable Electrode
Approximate Welding Conditions

Stock thickness, inch	Position	Preparation (see facing page)	Current, amperes d e	Electrode dia., inch	Wire speed, inches per minute	Argon flow, CFH	Arc volts	Number of passes	Weld speeds, inches per minute per pass	Electrode consumption, pounds per 100 feet
⅛	Flat		110	³⁄₆₄	175	30	20	1	24	2
	Horiz. & Vert.		100	³⁄₆₄	170	30	20	1	24	2
	Overhead		105	³⁄₆₄	170	40	20	1	24	2½
³⁄₁₆	Flat		170	³⁄₆₄	235	30	20	1	24	4½
	Horiz. & Vert.		150	³⁄₆₄	215	35	20	1	20	4½
	Overhead		160	³⁄₆₄	225	40	20	1	18	5
¼	Flat		200	¹⁄₁₆	170	40	25–29	1	24	8
	Horiz. & Vert.		170	¹⁄₁₆	150	45	25–29	3	24	8
	Overhead		180	¹⁄₁₆	160	50	25–29	3	24	10
⅜	Flat	A	290	¹⁄₁₆	265	50	25–29	2	24	18
		D	275	¹⁄₁₆	250	50	25–29	2	24	15
	Horiz. & Vert.	B	190	¹⁄₁₆	160	50	25–29	2	24	18
		E	170	¹⁄₁₆	150	50	25–29	2	24	15
	Overhead	C	200	¹⁄₁₆	170	50	25–29	5	24	23

Table continued on page 142.

Table 13

Edge Preparation

Stock thickness, inch	Flat	Horizontal and Vertical	Overhead
1/8			
3/16			
1/4			
3/8	A D	B E	C

Butt Welds—½″—3″
Inert Gas—Consumable Electrode
Approximate Welding Conditions

Stock thickness, inch	Position	Preparation (see facing page)	Current, amperes d c	Electrode dia., inch	Wire speed, inches per minute	Argon gas flow, CFH	Arc volts	Number of passes	Weld speed, inches per minute per pass	Electrode consumption, pounds per 100 feet
½	Flat	F	320	3/32	140	50	25–31	2	16	30
	Flat	G	290	3/32	130	50	25–31	2	16	31
	Flat	J	300	3/32	130	50	25–31	3	16	29
	Horiz. & Vert.	H	215	1/16	190	50	25–29	3	12	31
	Horiz. & Vert.	K	190	1/16	160	50	25–29	2	12	29
	Overhead	I	225	1/16	200	80	25–29	8	18	31
¾	Flat	G	350	3/32	150	60	25–31	4	16	62
	Flat	J	330	3/32	145	60	25–31	4	16	72
	Horiz. & Vert.	H	250	1/16	225	60	25–29	4	8	62
	Horiz. & Vert.	K	240	1/16	215	60	25–29	4	8	72
	Overhead	I	250	1/16	225	80	25–29	12	18	62
1	Flat	G	400	3/32	170	60	25–31	4	12	105
	Flat	M	400	3/32	170	60	25–31	5	12	180
	Flat	L	380	3/32	165	60	25–31	6	12	85
	Horiz. & Vert.	H	250	1/16	225	60	25–29	4	6	105
	Horiz. & Vert.	K	240	1/16	215	60	25–29	6	6	95
	Overhead	I	275	1/16	250	80	25–29	15	18	105
2	Flat	N	425	3/32	180	60	25–31	12	12	335
3	Flat	O	450	3/32	190	60	25–31	30	20	500

Table 13
(Concluded)

Edge Preparation

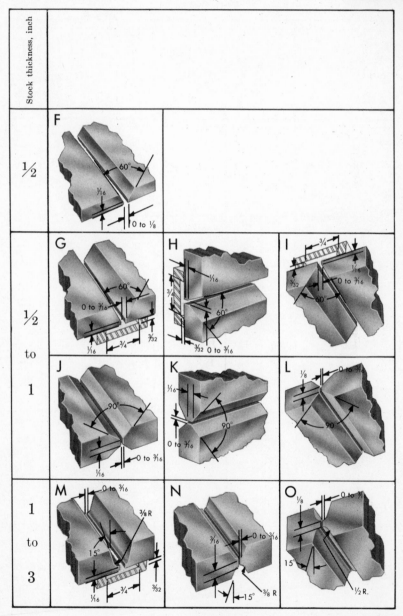

Stock thickness, inch			
½	F		
½ to 1	G	H	I
	J	K	L
1 to 3	M	N	O

Edge Welds
Inert Gas Consumable Electrode
Approximate Welding Conditions

Stock thickness, inch	Position	Current, amperes d c	Electrode dia., inch	Wire speed, inches per minute	Argon flow, CFH	Arc volts	Number of passes	Weld speed inches per minute per pass	Electrode consumption, pounds per 100 feet
1/8	Flat	110	3/64	175	30	20	1	30	4
	Horiz. & Vert.	100	3/64	170	30	20	1	24	4
	Overhead	100	3/64	170	40	20	1	24	4
3/16	Flat	170	3/64	235	30	20	1	30	8
	Horiz. & Vert.	150	3/64	215	35	20	1	24	8
	Overhead	160	3/64	225	40	20	1	24	8
1/4	Flat	200	1/16	170	40	25–29	1	30	15
	Horiz. & Vert.	170	1/16	150	45	25–29	1	24	15
	Overhead	180	1/16	160	50	25–29	1	24	15
3/8	Flat	250	1/16	220	50	25–29	3	30	34
	Horiz. & Vert.	170	1/16	150	50	25–29	3	24	34
	Overhead	180	1/16	160	60	25–29	3	24	34
1/2	Flat	290	3/32	130	50	25–31	3	16	60
	Horiz. & Vert.	190	1/16	160	50	25–29	3	12	60
	Overhead	200	1/16	170	70	25–29	5	18	60

Table **14**

Edge Preparation

Stock thickness, inch	Flat	Horizontal and Vertical	Overhead
1/8 to 1/4			
3/8 to 1/2			

Table **15**

Fillet Welds—Lap or Tee
Inert Gas Consumable Electrode

Edge Preparation

Flat	Horizontal	Vertical	Overhead
Weld			

Approximate Welding Conditions

Stock thickness, inch	Position	Current, amperes d c	Electrode dia., inch	Wire speed, inches per minute	Argon flow, CFH	Arc volts	Number of passes	Weld speed, inches per minute per pass	Electrode consumption, pounds per 100 feet
1/8	Flat	125	3/64	190	30	20	1	30	2
	Horiz. & Vert.	115	3/64	180	30	20	1	24	2
	Overhead	110	3/64	175	40	20	1	24	2
3/16	Flat	190	3/64	255	30	20	1	24	4½
	Horiz. & Vert.	165	3/64	230	35	20	1	20	4½
	Overhead	180	3/64	245	40	20	1	20	4½
1/4	Flat	225	1/16	195	40	25–29	1	24	7
	Horiz. & Vert.	200	1/16	170	45	25–29	1	20	7
	Overhead	200	1/16	170	50	25–29	1	20	7
3/8	Flat	300	1/16	275	50	25–29	3	30	17
	Horiz. & Vert.	200	1/16	170	50	25–29	3	24	17
	Overhead	220	1/16	195	60	25–29	3	24	17
1/2	Flat	340	3/32	145	50	25–31	3	16	30
	Horiz. & Vert.	225	1/16	200	50	25–29	3	12	30
	Overhead	230	1/16	205	70	25–29	5	18	30
3/4	Flat	375	3/32	160	60	25–31	4	16	66
	Horiz. & Vert.	260	1/16	235	60	25–29	4	8	66
	Overhead	275	1/16	250	80	25–29	10	18	66
1	Flat	425	3/32	180	60	25–31	4	8	120
	Horiz. & Vert.	260	1/16	235	60	25–29	6	6	120
	Overhead	290	1/16	265	80	25–29	14	18	120

Corner Welds
Inert Gas Consumable Electrode
Edge Preparation

Table 16

Flat	Horizontal	Vertical	Overhead

Approximate Welding Conditions

Stock thickness, inch	Position	Current, amperes d c	Electrode dia., inch	Wire speed, inches per minute	Argon flow, CFH	Arc volts	Number of passes	Weld speed, inches per minute per pass	Electrode consumption, pounds per 100 feet
$\frac{1}{8}$	Flat	110	$\frac{3}{64}$	175	30	20	1	30	2
	Horiz. & Vert.	100	$\frac{3}{64}$	170	30	20	1	24	2
	Overhead	100	$\frac{3}{64}$	170	40	20	1	24	2
$\frac{3}{16}$	Flat	170	$\frac{3}{64}$	235	30	20	1	30	$4\frac{1}{2}$
	Horiz. & Vert.	150	$\frac{3}{64}$	215	35	20	1	24	$4\frac{1}{2}$
	Overhead	160	$\frac{3}{64}$	225	40	20	1	24	$4\frac{1}{2}$
$\frac{1}{4}$	Flat	200	$\frac{1}{16}$	170	40	25–29	1	30	7
	Horiz. & Vert.	170	$\frac{1}{16}$	150	45	25–29	1	24	7
	Overhead	180	$\frac{1}{16}$	160	50	25–29	1	24	7
$\frac{3}{8}$	Flat	250	$\frac{1}{16}$	220	50	25–29	3	30	17
	Horiz. & Vert.	170	$\frac{1}{16}$	150	50	25–29	3	24	17
	Overhead	180	$\frac{1}{16}$	160	60	25–29	3	24	17
$\frac{1}{2}$	Flat	290	$\frac{3}{32}$	130	50	25–31	3	16	30
	Horiz. & Vert.	190	$\frac{1}{16}$	160	50	25–29	3	12	30
	Overhead	200	$\frac{1}{16}$	170	70	25–29	5	18	30
$\frac{3}{4}$	Flat	310	$\frac{3}{32}$	135	60	25–31	4	16	66
	Horiz. & Vert.	220	$\frac{1}{16}$	195	60	25–29	4	8	66

Resistance Weldability of Various Alloy Combinations[1]
Based on equal thickness

		Heat-treatable							
Alloy and Temper	(See notes on the facing page)	Al-clad 75S -T6	75S -T6	63S -T5 -T6	61S -T4 -T6	Al-clad 24S -T3 -T4	24S -T3 -T4	Al-clad 14S -T4 -T6	4S -T4 -T6
2S–O 3S–O	Weld			C	C				
	Preclean			B	B				
	Res. Corr.			A	A				
2S 3S –H12, –H14, –H16, –H18	Weld			A	A				
	Preclean			A	B				
	Res. Corr.			A	A				
S–O	Weld			C	C				
	Preclean			B	B				
	Res. Corr.			A	A				
4S–H32, –H34, –H36, –H38	Weld			A	A				
	Preclean			B	B				
	Res. Corr.			A	A				
50S–O	Weld			C	C				
	Preclean			B	B				
	Res. Corr.			A	A				
50S–H32, –H34, –H36, –H38	Weld			A	A				
	Preclean			B	B				
	Res. Corr.			A	A				
52S–O	Weld			C	C				
	Preclean			B	B				
	Res. Corr.			A	A				
52S–H32, –H34, –H36, –H38	Weld	B	B	A	A	B	B	B	B
	Preclean	B	B	B	B	B	B	B	B
	Res. Corr.	A	B	A	A	A	B	A	B
56S–O	Weld			C	C				
	Preclean			B	B				
	Res. Corr.			A	A				
56S A54S –H32, –H34, –H36, –H38	Weld			A	A				
	Preclean			B	B				
	Res. Corr.			A	A				
14S–T4, –T6	Weld	B	B	B	B	B	B	B	B
	Preclean	B	B	B	B	B	B	B	B
	Res. Corr.	B	B	B	B	B	B	A	B
Alclad 14S–T4, –T6	Weld	B	B	B	B	B	B	B	
	Preclean	B	B	B	B	B	B	B	
	Res. Corr.	A	B	A	A	A	B	A	
24S–T3, –T4	Weld	B	B	B	B	B	B		
	Preclean	B	B	B	B	B	B		
	Res. Corr.	B	B	B	B	B	B		
Alclad 24S–T3, –T4	Weld	B	B	B	B	B			
	Preclean	B	B	B	B	B			
	Res. Corr.	A	B	A	A	A			
61S–T4, –T6	Weld	B	B	A	B				
	Preclean	B	B	B	B				
	Res. Corr.	A	B	A	A				
63S–T5, –T6	Weld	B	B	A					
	Preclean	B	B	B					
	Res. Corr.	A	B	A					
75S–T6	Weld	B	B						
	Preclean	B	B						
	Res. Corr.	B	B						
Alclad 75S–T6	Weld	B							
	Preclean	B							
	Res. Corr.	A							

Nonheat-treatable (rows 2S–O through 56S/A54S)
Heat-treatable (rows 14S–T4 through Alclad 75S–T6)

[1] The blank spaces in this table represent seldom used combinations of alloys. Information on these alloy combinations can be obtained by contacting Aluminum Company of America.

Table **17**

Alloy and Temper	Nonheat-treatable									
	56S or A54S -H32 -H34 -H36 -H38	56S -O	52S -H32 -H34 -H36 -H38	52S -O	50S -H32 -H34 -H36 -H38	50S -O	4S -H32 -H34 -H36 -H38	4S -O	2S -H12 -H14 -H16 -H18	2S-O 3S-O
2S-O / 3S-O			C/B/A	D/B/A	C/A/A	D/A/A	C/A/A	D/A/A	C/A/A	D/A/A
2S 3S }-H32, -H34, -H36, -H38			A/B/A	C/B/A	A/B/A	A/B/A	A/A/A	C/B/A	A/A/A	
4S-O	C/B/A		C/B/A	D/B/A	C/B/A	D/B/A	C/A/A	D/A/A		
4S-H32, -H34, -H36, -H38	A/B/A		A/B/A	D/B/A	A/B/A	C/B/A	A/A/A			
50S-O			C/B/A	D/B/A	C/B/A	D/B/A				
50S-H32, -H34, -H36, -H38	A/B/A		A/B/A	C/B/A	A/B/A					
52S-O			C/B/A	D/B/A						
52S-H32, -H34, -H36, -H38	A/B/A		A/B/A							
56S-O	C/A/A	D/A/A								
56S A54S }-H32, -H34, -H36, -H38	A/A/A									

EASE OF WELDING

A. Good welds can be made over a wide range of machine settings.
B. Makes good welds, but special practices are required and can be welded only over narrow range of machine settings.
C. Can be welded, but material too soft to obtain consistent weld strength.
D. Difficult to weld—not recommended.

PRECLEANING

A. Easy to clean or frequently needs no cleaning.
B. Chemical or mechanical precleaning necessary to make sound and consistent welds.

RESISTANCE TO CORROSION

A. Corrosion resistance of weld zone equal to parent metal.
B. Corrosion resistance of weld zone not as good as parent metal.

Temper	Thickness of parts, inch				
	Up to 0.020	0.021– 0.032	0.033– 0.064	0.065– 0.094	0.095– 0.125
Annealed and as-extruded . . .	2	3	4	4	..
Intermediate tempers of nonheat-treated alloys	2	3	3	4	6
Heat-treated	1	2	3	4	6

① If a flat surface is required on one side of the work, one tip is made to the above radius, and the other electrode has either a flat or 10-inch radius tip.

Table **19**

**Minimum Shear Strength of Spot
Welds in Aluminum Alloys**

Thinnest sheet, in joint, inch	2S–H14 2S–H18 Lb/spot	3S–H12 3S–H18 52S–0 Lb/spot	52S–H32 52S–H38 61S–T4 61S–T6 50S–H34 Lb/spot	24S–T3 A1clad 24S–T3 75S–T6 A1clad 75S–T6 Lb/spot
.016	40	70	98	108
.020	55	100	132	140
.025	70	145	175	185
.032	110	210	235	260
.040	150	300	310	345
.051	205	410	442	480
.064	280	565	625	690
.081	420	775	865	1050
.102	520	950	1200	1535
.125	590	1000	1625	2120

Approximate Spot Welding Schedule
for Single-Phase Machines

Table **20**

Thinnest sheet in joint, inch	Electrode diameter, inch	Electrode tip radii, inches (top and bottom)	Net electrode force during weld, lb	Welding time cycles (for 60~ supply)	Welding current, amperes	Diameter of weld nugget, inch
0.016	5/8	1—Flat	320	4	15,000	0.110
0.020	5/8	1—Flat	340	5	18,000	0.125
0.025	5/8	2—Flat	390	6	21,800	0.140
0.032	5/8	2—Flat	500	6	26,000	0.160
0.040	5/8	3—Flat	600	8	30,700	0.180
0.051	5/8	3—Flat	660	8	33,000	0.210
0.064	5/8	3—Flat	750	10	35,900	0.250
0.072	5/8	4—4	800	10	38,000	0.275
0.081	7/8	4—4	860	10	41,800	0.300
0.091	7/8	6—6	950	12	46,000	0.330
0.102	7/8	6—6	1050	15	56,000	0.360
0.125	7/8	6—6	1300	15	76,000	0.425

Approximate Spot Welding Schedule
for Condenser Stored-Energy Machines

Table **21**

Thinnest sheet in joint, inch	Electrode diameter, inch	Electrode tip radii, inches	Net electrode force, lb — Weld	Net electrode force, lb — Forge	Condenser capacity microfarads	Condenser charge, kilovolts	Transformer ratio	Total energy watt-sec.	Diameter of weld nugget, inch
0.020	5/8	3	376	692	240	2.15	300:1	555	0.125
0.032	5/8	3	580	1300	240	2.7	300:1	875	0.160
0.040	5/8	3	680	1580	360	2.55	300:1	1172	0.180
0.051	5/8	3	890	2100	600	2.56	300:1	1952	0.210
0.064	5/8	3	1080	2680	720	2.7	300:1	2622	0.250
0.072	5/8	3	1230	3150	960	2.75	450:1	3630	0.275
0.081	7/8	3	1550	4000	1440	2.7	450:1	5250	0.300
0.091	7/8	3	1830	4660	1920	2.65	450:1	6750	0.330
0.102	7/8	3	2025	5100	2520	2.7	450:1	9180	0.360

Table 22

Approximate Spot Welding Schedule for Three-Phase Rectifier-Type Machines

Thinnest sheet in joint, inch	Electrode diameter, inch	Electrode tip radii, inches	Net electrode force, lb		Time, cycles (for 60~ supply)		Current, amperes		Diameter of weld nugget, inch
			Weld	Forge	Weld	Post heat	Weld	Post heat	
0.016	5/8	3	440	1000	1	None	19,000	None	0.110
0.020	5/8	3	520	1150	1	None	22,000	None	0.125
0.032	5/8	3	670	1540	2	None	28,000	None	0.160
0.040	5/8	3	730	1800	3	None	32,000	None	0.180
0.051	5/8	8	900	2250	4	4	37,000	30,000	0.210
0.064	5/8	8	1100	2900	5	5	43,000	36,000	0.250
0.072	5/8	8	1190	3240	6	7	48,000	38,000	0.275
0.081	7/8	8	1460	3800	7	9	52,000	42,000	0.300
0.091	7/8	8	1700	4300	8	11	56,000	45,000	0.330
0.102	7/8	8	1900	5000	9	14	61,000	49,000	0.360
0.125	7/8	8	2500	6500	10	22	69,000	54,000	0.425

Table 23

Approximate Spot Welding Schedule for 3-Phase Frequency-Converter Machines

Thinnest sheet in joint, inch	Electrode diameter, inch	Electrode tip radii, inches	Net electrode force, lb		Approximate time, cycles (for 60~ supply)		Approximate current, amperes		Approximate diameter of weld nugget, inch
			Weld	Forge	Weld	Post heat	Weld	Post heat	
0.020	5/8	3	500	None	1/2	None	26,000	None	0.125
0.025	5/8	3	500	1500	1	3	34,000	8,500	0.140
0.032	5/8	4	700	1800	1	4	36,000	9,000	0.160
0.040	5/8	4	800	2000	1	4	42,000	12,600	0.180
0.051	5/8	4	900	2300	1	5	46,000	13,800	0.210
0.064	5/8	6	1300	3000	2	5	54,000	18,900	0.250
0.072	5/8	6	1600	3600	2	6	61,000	21,350	0.275
0.081	7/8	6	2000	4300	3	6	65,000	22,750	0.300
0.091	7/8	6	2400	5300	3	8	75,000	30,000	0.330
0.102	7/8	8	2800	6800	3	8	85,000	34,000	0.360
0.125	7/8	8	4000	9000	4	10	100,000	45,000	0.425

Approximate Welding Schedule
for Gas-Tight Seam Welds with A C Machines [1]

Table **24**

Thickness t, inch	Spots per inch	"On" plus "off" time[2] cycles	Wheel speed,[3] ft/min.	"On" time, cycles Min.	"On" time, cycles Max.[4]	Welding[5] pressure, pounds	Welding[5] current, amperes	Width of weld, inch
0.010	25	3½	3.4	½	1	420	19,500	0.08
0.016	21	3½	4.1	½	1	500	22,000	0.09
0.020	20	4½	3.3	½	1½	540	24,000	0.10
0.025	18	5½	3.0	1	1½	600	26,000	0.11
0.032	16	5½	3.4	1	1½	690	29,000	0.13
0.040	14	7½	2.9	1½	2½	760	32,000	0.14
0.051	12	9½	2.6	1½	3	860	36,000	0.16
0.064	10	11½	2.6	2	3½	960	38,500	0.19
0.081	9	15½	2.1	3	5	1090	41,000	0.22
0.102	8	20½	1.8	4	6½	1230	43,000	0.26
0.125	7	28½	1.5	5½	9½	1350	45,000	0.32

[1] Wheel electrodes and work must be cooled with from 2 to 3 gallons of water per minute.
[2] Use next higher full cycle setting if timer is not equipped to give antipole starting of current.
[3] Wheel speed is adjusted to give desired spots per inch.
[4] "On" time must be set at full cycle setting if "on" plus "off" time is set at full cycle setting.
[5] Welding pressure and welding current are adjusted to give desired width of weld. Values are for 52S-H34 aluminum alloy. Use lower pressures for 52S-O or 3S-H14 aluminum alloys.

Suggested Minimum Joint Overlap and Weld Spacing

Table **25**

Thinnest sheet in joint, inch	Minimum joint overlap, inch	Minimum weld spacing, inch
.016	5/16	3/8
.020	3/8	3/8
.025	3/8	3/8
.032	½	½
.040	9/16	½
.051	5/8	5/8
.064	3/4	5/8
.072	13/16	3/4
.081	7/8	3/4
.091	15/16	7/8
.102	1	1
.125	1⅛	1¼

| Table **26** | | **Strength of Flash Welds in Several Aluminum Alloys**① | | |

Alloy	Temper welded	Post weld heat treatment	Tensile strength, psi	Elongation, % in 4d
3S	–H16	No	21,800	9.2
61S	–T6	No	38,900	6.6
61S	–T6	Yes	47,900	13.6
24S	–T3	No	67,800	8.1
24S	–T3	Yes	65,300	8.9
75S	–T6	No	75,300	3.5
75S	–T6	Yes	78,900	4.1

①Tests made on flash welded ⅝-inch diameter rod.

| Table **27** | | **Approximate Conditions for Metal Arc and Carbon Arc Welding** |

Metal thickness, inch	Electrode or filler diameter, inch	Approximate current, amperes	Number of passes		Filler metal consumption, pounds per 100 ft		
			Butt	Lap and Fillet	Butt	Lap	Fillet
0.081	⅛	60	1	1	4.7	5.3	6.3
0.102	⅛	70	1	1	5.0	5.7	6.3
0.125	⅛	80	1	1	5.7	6.3	6.3
0.156	⅛	100	1	1	6.3	6.5	6.5
0.188	5⁄32	125	1	1	8.7	9.0	9.0
0.250	3⁄16	160	1	1	12	12	12
0.375	{ 3⁄16 for laps and fillets, ¼ for butts }	200	2	3	25	29	35
0.500	{ 3⁄16 for laps and fillets, ¼ for butts }	300	3	3	35	35	35
1.00	5⁄16	450	3	3	130	150	150
2.00	5⁄16 and ⅜	550	8	8	400	450	450

Approximate Conditions for Atomic-Hydrogen Arc Welding[1]

Table **28**

Thickness, inch	Electrode size	Current, amperes	Filler rod diameter, inch
$\frac{1}{16}$ to $\frac{1}{8}$	$\frac{1}{16}$	20–25	$\frac{3}{32}$
$\frac{1}{8}$ to $\frac{3}{16}$	$\frac{1}{16}$	25–35	$\frac{1}{8}$
$\frac{3}{16}$ to $\frac{3}{8}$	$\frac{1}{16}$ or $\frac{1}{8}$	35–40	$\frac{1}{8}$ or $\frac{5}{32}$
$\frac{3}{8}$ to $\frac{5}{8}$	$\frac{1}{8}$	40–50	$\frac{3}{16}$
$\frac{5}{8}$ to $\frac{3}{4}$	$\frac{1}{8}$	60–80	$\frac{3}{16}$ or $\frac{1}{4}$

[1] To obtain maximum welding speeds, sections $\frac{3}{8}$ inch or more in thickness should be preheated to a temperature of 600 to 700°F, and maintained in this temperature range during welding. Sections lighter than $\frac{3}{8}$ inch in thickness are rapidly heated by the welding arc, and preheating is not ordinarily advantageous.

Approximate Conditions for Gas Welding

Table **29**

Metal thickness, inch	Oxyhydrogen			Oxyacetylene		
	Diameter of orifice in tip, inch	Oxygen pressure, psi	Hydrogen pressure, psi	Diameter of orifice in tip, inch	Oxygen pressure, psi	Acetylene pressure, psi
.020	0.035	1	1	0.025	1	1
.032	0.045	1	1	0.035	1	1
.051	0.065	2	1	0.045	2	2
.081	0.075	2	1	0.055	3	3
$\frac{1}{8}$	0.095	3	2	0.065	4	4
$\frac{1}{4}$	0.105	4	2	0.075	5	5
$\frac{5}{16}$	0.115	4	2	0.085	5	5
$\frac{3}{8}$	0.125	5	3	0.095	6	6
$\frac{5}{8}$	0.150	8	6	0.105	7	7

Table 30

Strength and Ductility of Welded Butt Joints[1]

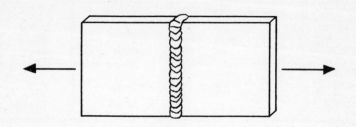

Alloy		Specified minimum tensile strength of parent material psi		Average tensile strength across weld, psi	Average free-bend elongation, per cent
Parent material	Filler wire	Annealed	Heat-Treated		
NON HEAT-TREATABLE ALLOYS					
DD1S	DD1S	9,500	..	9,800	63
2S	2S	11,000	..	13,400	54
3S	2S	14,000	..	16,000	58
4S	4S	23,000	..	27,500	26
52S	52S	25,000	..	28,200	39
A54S	A54S	30,000	..	33,300	39
56S	56S	35,000	..	38,300	31
XC56S	XC56S	35,000	..	40,200	34
HEAT-TREATABLE ALLOYS (Not Heat-Treated After Welding)					
14S-T6	43S	..	64,000	33,900	9
61S-T6	43S	..	42,000	27,200	16
62S-T6	43S	..	42,000	27,200	16
63S-T5	43S	..	22,000	20,000	..
63S-T6	43S	..	32,000	20,000	..
63S-T83	43S	..	33,000	20,000	..
63S-T831	43S	..	28,000	20,000	..
63S-T832	43S	..	40,000	20,000	..
HEAT-TREATABLE ALLOYS (Heat-Treated and Aged After Welding)					
14S-T6	43S	..	64,000	51,500	5
61S-T6	43S	..	42,000	43,500	11
62S-T6	43S	..	42,000	43,500	11

[1]Made by the Argon-Shielded Tungsten Arc or the Argon-Shielded Consumable Electrode Method.

Shear Strength of Fillet Welds

Table 31

Aluminum alloy		Average shear strength, psi	
Plate	Filler metal	Longitudinal	Transverse
2S or 3S	2S	12,000	14,000
52S	52S	. .	21,000
A54S	A54S	23,000	30,000
61S-T6①	43S	18,000	22,000

①Without any subsequent thermal treatment.

Commonly Used Specifications for the Control and Inspection of Aluminum Alloy Weldments

Table 32

Title	Origin and Number
Aluminum and Aluminum Alloy Welding Rod	Federal QQ-R-566
Electrodes Welding, Bare and Aluminum Alloys	Military E-16053 B (Ships)
Flux—Welding Aluminum (Alcoa No. 22)	MIL-F-6939
Flux—Aluminum Brazing (Alcoa No. 33)	SAE–AMS 3412
Flux—Aluminum Welding (Alcoa No. 22)	SAE–AMS 3414
Aluminum Alloy Brazing Wire—No. 716	SAE–AMS 4184A
Aluminum Alloy Brazing Wire—No. 718	SAE–AMS 4185
Aluminum Alloy Welding Wire—43S	SAE–AMS 4190A
Tentative Specifications for Brazing Filler Metal	ASTM–B 260-52T
Tentative Specifications for Aluminum and Aluminum Alloy Welding Rod and Bare Electrode	AWS A5.10-54T ASTM B285-54T
Welding—Aluminum and Magnesium Alloys— Spot and Seam	Military MIL-W-6860
ASME Boiler and Pressure Vessel Code	Sec. IX—Nonferrous Welding Qualification
Porosity Standards of the Boiler Construction Code	ASME—Aug. 24, 1951
Test—Aircraft Welding Operators—Certification	Military MIL-T-5021
Spot and Seam Welding of Aluminum and Magnesium Alloys	Military MIL-W-6860

ALCOA
WELDING, BRAZING AND
SOLDERING MATERIALS

FLUXES

Flux Number	*Use*	*Color*
No. 22	Torch Flame Welding	Pink
No. 24	Automatic Carbon Arc Welding . . .	Pink
No. 27	Flux Coated Electrode Arc Welding .	Green
No. 30	Furnace Brazing	Orange
No. 33	Furnace and Torch Flame Brazing . .	Light Green
No. 34	Furnace and Dip Brazing	Yellow
No. 53	Furnace and Dip Brazing	Pale Blue
No. 64	Soldering	Pale Brown

NOTE: Flux is packed in 8-oz, 1-lb, 5 lb glass bottles, or 50-lb, 150-lb drums.

FILLER MATERIALS

Alloy	*Use*	*Standard Sizes*
2S-43S-A54S	Welding Filler Wire . . .	$\frac{3}{32}$, $\frac{1}{8}$, $\frac{5}{32}$, $\frac{3}{16}$, $\frac{1}{4}$, $\frac{5}{16}$[1] inch diameter
2S-43S-A54S	I.G. Welding Electrodes .	.030, .045, $\frac{1}{16}$, $\frac{3}{32}$, $\frac{1}{8}$[1] inch diameter
No. 718 Brazing Wire		$\frac{3}{32}$, $\frac{1}{8}$, $\frac{5}{32}$, $\frac{3}{16}$, inch[1] diameter .020 x 2-inch w i d e[2] flattened wire
No. 804 Solder		$\frac{1}{8}$-inch diameter wire[3]
No. 802 Solder		$\frac{1}{4}$-inch stick

[1] 50 lb coils or 36-in. straight lengths.
[2] Coiled strip.
[3] 1 lb spools.

PRODUCTS
SOLD BY ALCOA

NOTE: This list of products contains a minimum number of cross-referenced items necessary for the readers' convenience. Many products—cast, forged, draw pressed, extruded, impact extruded, screw machine and job shop—are produced to customers' specifications. Your nearest Alcoa sales office can be helpful in recommending the most efficient application of these products to your needs.

ACSR (aluminum cable steel reinforced)

Alclad aluminum
Pipe
Plate
Sheet
Tube
Wire

Aluminas (see Chemicals)

Angles

Bar
Hexagonal
Rectangular
Special shapes for screw machine stock

Barrels

Beams

Beer barrels

Billets or blooms for wrought aluminum products

Bolts

Brazing flux and wire

Bus (see Electrical conductors)

Cable (see Electrical conductors)

Carboys

Casting alloy ingot

Castings
Die
Permanent mold
Plaster mold
Sand
Semipermanent mold

Channels

Chemicals
Aluminas
Activated
Calcined
Hydrated
Low soda
Tabular

Chemicals *(Concluded)*
  Aluminum fluoride
  Cryolite
  Fluoboric acid
  Gallium
  Sodium acid fluoride
  Sodium fluoride
Circles, sheet and plate
Closures, bottle
  Sealing machines
Coiled sheet
Coiled tube
Cold-headed products
Collapsible tubes for packaging tooth paste, drugs, calking compounds, greases, etc.
Conduit, rigid
Copings
Corrugated sheet
Cryolite insecticide
Die castings
Draw press products
Drums, shipping
Electrical conductors
  Cable, all aluminum or ACSR (aluminum cable steel reinforced)
  Cable fittings and accessories
  Buses
    Channels
    Flat
    Tubular
  Bus fittings and accessories
  Fuse wire
  Wire
Electrical metallic tubing
Extruded shapes

Fasteners
  Bolts
  Nails
  Nuts
  Rivets
  Screws
  Screw machine products
  Washers
Finishes
  Alumilite
  Alrok
  Electroplating
  Other finishes are available
Fluoboric acid
Fluorides (see Chemicals)
Foil
  Condenser
  Insulating
  Household
  Milkbottle hoods
  Packaging
Forgings, hammer and press
Fuse wire
Gallium
Grained ingot
Gravel stops
H-beams
Hammer forgings
Handrail pipe and fittings
I-beams
Impact extrusion products
Ingot
  Casting alloy
  Metallurgical granulated
Insecticide, cryolite
Irrigation pipe
Continued on next page

160

Kettles

Lighting sheet

Lithograph sheet

Milkbottle hoods, foil

Moldings (see Extruded
   shapes)

Nails

Nuts

Paint pigment, aluminum

Patterned sheet

Permanent mold castings

Piano plates

Pig

Pigments
   Powder and paste for paint
      and printing ink

Pipe (see also Tube)
   Construction
   Handrail, and fittings
   Irrigation
   Standard, and fittings

Pistons

Plate (see sheet)
   Alclad
   Circles
   Odd-shaped blanks with
      sheared or sawed edges
   Rectangular
   Tapered
   Tread

Plaster mold castings

Powder, aluminum (see also
   Pigments)
   Dusting
   Rubber Compounding

Press forgings

Process equipment (made to
   specification)

Rectangular tube

Rectanglar wire, rod and bar

Reflector sheet

Rivets and rivet wire

Rod
   Redraw
   Round

Roofing sheet

Sand castings

Screening wire

Screws
   Machine
   Sheet metal
   Special types
   Wood

Screw machine products
   (made to specification)

Screw machine stock (see also
   Rod, Bar)

Seals (bottle closures) and
   sealing machines

Semipermanent mold castings

Sheet (see also Plate)
   Alclad
   Circles
   Coiled
   Flat
   Odd-shaped blanks with
      sheared or sawed edges
   Specialty sheet
      Alumilite
      Brazing
      Corrugated

Sheet *(Concluded)*
  Specialty sheet
    Lithograph
    Patterned
    Recording circles
    Reflector
    Roofing
    Siding
    Tapered
  Shipping containers
    Beer barrels
    Carboys
    Drums
Siding sheet
Sodium acid fluoride
Sodium fluoride
Solder and flux
Spandrels
Square tube
Structural assemblies (made to specification)
Structural shapes (rolled and extruded)
Tanks, welded
Tees
Thin-wall containers
Thread lubricant and compound
Thresholds
Tool and jig plates
Tooth paste tubes
Tread plate

Tube (see also Pipe)
  Alclad
  Coiled
  Electrical metallic
  Heat exchanger
  Round
  Square
  Special shapes
Tubes, collapsible
Welding materials
  Flux
  Wire
Washers
Wheels, truck, trailer and bus
  Disc
  Spoke
Window sills
Wire
  Alclad
  Flattened
  Hexagonal
  Rectangular
  Round
  Rivet
  Special shapes
  Square
  Welding
Wire, electrical (see Electrical conductors)
Zees

COMMERCIAL FORMS OF MAGNESIUM PRODUCTS sold by Alcoa include Castings, Forgings, Sheet and Plate, Extrusions, Tube and Pipe, Rod and Bar, and Structural Shapes. Also available are Pipe Line and Water Tank Anodes.

Welding Alcoa Aluminum

List of Figures

List of Tables

List of Tables—Continued

List of Photographs

APPLICATIONS

TUNGSTEN ARC WELDING

CONSUMABLE ELECTRODE WELDING

SPOT AND SEAM WELDING

List of Photographs—Continued

List of Photographs—Continued

Welding Alcoa Aluminum

Index

ALCOA SALES OFFICES

ABERDEEN, S. D.	304 Western Union Building
AKRON 8, OHIO	506 Akron Savings & Loan Building
ALBANY 7, N. Y.	90 State Street
ALLENTOWN, PA.	1132 Hamilton Street
ATLANTA 3, GA.	1800 Rhodes-Haverty Building
BALTIMORE 1, MD.	400 Baltimore Life Building
BIRMINGHAM 3, ALA.	505 First National Building
BOSTON 16, MASS.	20 Providence Street, Park Square
BRIDGEPORT 4, CONN.	Atlantic Street
BUFFALO 7, N. Y.	1880 Elmwood Avenue
CHARLOTTE 2, N. C.	616 Johnston Building
CHATTANOOGA 1, TENN.	1205 Volunteer Building
CHICAGO 11, ILL.	520 North Michigan Avenue
CINCINNATI 2, OHIO	801 Enquirer Building
CLEVELAND 13, OHIO	1450 Terminal Tower
COLUMBUS 15, OHIO	40 South Third Street Building
DALLAS 2, TEXAS	301 Thomas Building
DAVENPORT, IOWA	503 Kahl Building
DAYTON 5, OHIO	207 Northtown Arcade
DENVER 18, COLO.	1112 East 18th Avenue
DES MOINES, IOWA	410 Walnut Building
DETROIT 2, MICH.	610 New Center Building
EVANSVILLE 10, IND.	207 Kinkel Building
FORT WAYNE, IND.	930 Lincoln Bank Tower
GRAND RAPIDS 2, MICH.	812 Michigan National Bank Building
HARTFORD 3, CONN.	Capitol Building, 410 Asylum Street
HOUSTON 2, TEXAS	1804 Commerce Building
INDIANAPOLIS 4, IND.	303 Guaranty Building
JACKSON, MICH.	1405 National Bank Building
KANSAS CITY 5, MO.	2300 Power & Light Building
LOS ANGELES 17, CALIF.	1145 Wilshire Boulevard
LOUISVILLE 2, KY.	1152 Starks Building
MEMPHIS 3, TENN.	2802 Sterick Building
MIAMI 32, FLA.	1605 Alfred I. du Pont Building
MILWAUKEE 2, WIS.	735 North Water Street
MINNEAPOLIS 2, MINN.	1060 Northwestern Bank Building
NEWARK 2, N. J.	744 Broad Street
NEW ORLEANS 12, LA.	627 Whitney Building
NEW YORK 17, N. Y.	230 Park Avenue
OKLAHOMA CITY 2, OKLA.	111 N.W. 23rd Street
OMAHA 2, NEB.	708 Omaha National Bank Building
PEORIA 1, ILL.	725 Commercial Bank Building
PHILADELPHIA 9, PA.	123 S. Broad Street
PITTSBURGH 19, PA.	1501 Alcoa Building
PONTIAC 15, MICH.	301 Pontiac State Bank Building
PORTLAND 4, ORE.	1115 U. S. National Bank Building
PROVIDENCE 3, R. I.	815 Industrial Trust Building
RICHMOND 19, VA.	712 Southern States Building
ROCHESTER 4, N. Y.	1331 Lincoln Alliance Bank Building
ST. LOUIS 8, MO.	10th Floor, Continental Building
SAN FRANCISCO 4, CALIF.	615 Russ Building
SEATTLE 1, WASH.	1411 Fourth Avenue Building
SOUTH BEND 1, IND.	805 J.M.S. Building
SPRINGFIELD 3, MASS.	232 Tarbell-Watters Building
SYRACUSE 2, N. Y.	1018 State Tower Building
TAMPA 2, FLA.	227 First National Building
TOLEDO 4, OHIO	1801 Ohio Building
WASHINGTON 6, D. C.	1200 Ring Building
WICHITA 2, KAN.	1011 Central Building
WILMINGTON 1, DEL.	301 Delaware Trust Building
WORCESTER 8, MASS.	22 Pleasant Street
YORK, PA.	205 Manufacturers Building

ALUMINUM COMPANY OF AMERICA
General Offices, Alcoa Building, Pittsburgh 19, Pa.